Science and Technology Illustrated

The World Around Us

Science
Technology

The World Around Us

and

Illustrated

17 68

Encyclopaedia Britannica, Inc.

CHICAGO

AUCKLAND · GENEVA

LONDON · MANILA

PARIS · ROME

SEOUL · SYDNEY

TOKYO · TORONTO

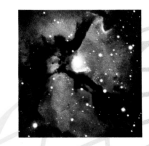

Preface

Science and Technology Illustrated: The World Around Us is an entirely new publication on an entirely new plan.

Encyclopedists employ various metaphors, or pictures, to suggest and sum up their work. The editors of *Encyclopaedia Britannica* speak of a Great Circle of Knowledge, which their encyclopaedia both describes and reports. The editors of *Science and Technology Illustrated* have built this set of books on the idea of the universe as a great organism that works and works well.

That the universe works cannot be questioned. We are a part of it, it operates upon us, and we operate within it. The ways in which it works are often puzzling, and sometimes still unknown.

Yet a great deal is known about how the world works—the world as a whole, and the thousands and thousands of separate parts of it that have independent life and being. Every article in *Science and Technology Illustrated* attempts to answer questions about how the world, or some part of the world, works. These parts may be inanimate: stars or electrical forces or elements or mathematical relations. Or they may be animate: species of plants or animals, or individual living things—a man or a woman or a child, or a single living cell.

Everything that exists operates or works, in some sense of the words, within the great system that is the world. If it did not work it would not be; if it had no reason to be it could not continue long in existence. But things work in very different ways, as the distinction between inanimate and animate beings suggests. And therefore the answers to questions about how things work are not always the same.

To view the world or universe as a living, operating system or organism is but one way to view it. The universe can also be viewed as something dead, like a butterfuly pinned to a sheet of white paper. The first way of looking at things is intellectually more exciting, and in many ways much more fun. And the editors of *Science and Technology Illustrated* had fun in mind when they made this set of books. They had fun creating it, and they hope all its readers have fun using it. If that happens, then their effort will have been amply rewarded.

THE EDITORS

Editorial Staff

Science & Technology Illustrated is a thoroughly modern work which involved the efforts of two major publishers on two continents. The text, commissioned by Encyclopaedia Britannica, Inc. in the U.S.A., was written by professional science writers with the advice and assistance of American scientific consultants. The illustrations were created by

FOR ENCYCLOPAEDIA BRITANNICA, INC.

General Editorial Consultant	Charles Van Doren
Project Coordinator	James Ertel
Editorial Assistant	Ines Baptist
General Editor (Text)	Mary Lee Grisanti
Copy Chief	John Berseth
Managing Editor	Robert Crease
Editorial Staff	Corinna Gardner
	Dale McAdoo
	Charles Mann
	Graham Yost

General Editor (Captions) James Hansen   **Caption Staff** Stephen Dembner
Mary Gailbraith
Alexandra Richardson

Copy Editors

Jean Brody	Catherine Gontrum	Shari Perretti
Leslie Deutsch	Andrea Kantor	Jacqueling Rivkin
Josh Eppinger	Rachel Markowitz	David Sider
Marguerite Feitlowitz	Sandy Matthews	Fay Webern
Rochelle Goldstein	Dolores Oetting	Lorraine Zuckerman

Authors

Christian Angermann	Barbara George	Deborah Lumpee
Donald Antrim	Ellen Goldensohn	Charles Mann
Timothy Bay	Peter Gyallay-Pap	Robert MacVicar
Trudy Bell	Steve Hall	Dale McAdoo
Shelley Berc	James Harris	Fred Nadis
David Black	Doug Henwood	Peter Oberlink
Diane Blanchard	David Herndon	Robert Salter
Bonnie Borenstein	Paul Hoeffel	Sandra Sharp
Judith Brister	Andrea Kantor	George Shea
Jean Brody	Jonathan Katz	Howard Smith
Serena Cha	Jim Keegan	Zev Trachtenberg
Robert Crease	Philippa Keil	Vieri Tucci
Peter Cunningham	Percy Knauth	Edit Emili Villareal
Rhodes Fairbridge	Barry Koffler	Veronica Visser
Marguerite Feitlowitz	Barbara Kopit	Graham Yost
Jean Grasso-Fitzpatrick	Paulette Licitra	Sasha Zeif
Corinna Gardner	Becky London	

Production: Graphic Design Studios   Typography: World Composition Services, Inc.

English Language Edition Produced by ACCOLADE ENTERPRISES, INC.

skilled artists commissioned by Gruppo Editoriale Fabbri in Italy. The captions for this edition were written by professional American science writers living in Italy and working in conjunction with the Italian illustrators. The staffs on the two continents are as follows:

FOR GRUPPO EDITORIALE FABBRI

Editorial Director	Eugenio De Rosa
Scientific Editorial Coordinator	Ugo Scaioni
Editorial Staff	Cesi Alessi
	Mario Biolcati
	Anna De Benedetti
	Margherita Finozzi
	Andrea Fioroni
	Edda Fonda
	Marina Giorgetti
	Rita Toninelli
	Logical Studio Communication

International Coordinator Anna Maria Mascheroni   **Scientific Consultant** Franco Potenza
Art Director Cesare Baroni   **Graphics Coordinator** Luciano Boschini

Graphics and Layout   Agostino Albicocco   Giuliana Colombo
Ornella Banfi   Bruno De Checchi
Carmen Boveri   Emilio Valenti

Editorial Secretaries   Maria Granzia Boeri   **Foreign Office**   Ludovica Osimo
Antonia Locatelli
Editorial Planning   Tina Cassini   **Picture Research**   Ludovica Pomini
Ornella Zoia   Evelina Rossetti
Logical Studio Communication

Quality Control   Silvano Caldara

Illustrators

Giorgio Alisi	Tina Mariani	Studio Erre A 70
Marina Bighellini	Michelangelo Miani	Studio Pitre
Renata Bonzo	Elisa Patergnani	Studio Prisma
Genny Buccheri	Gabriele Pozzi	Studio Prograf
Andrea Corbella	Sergio Quaranta	Studio Sun-Fog
Luciano Corbella	Aldo Ripamonti	Studio U.T.S.
Riccardo Ferrari	Ferdinando Russo	Tiger Tateishi
Gabriella Gallerani	Mario Russo	Triagono Illustrazione
Ezio Giglioli	Logical Studio Communication	Masayoshi Yamamoto

Consultants

Andrew Abrahams, M.D.
Bedford Stuyvescent Hospital

Nancy Akre
Cooper-Hewitt Museum

Dr. Neil Baggett
Brookhaven National Laboratory

J. Thomas Barnard, M.D.
Columbia University

William Bates
Computer consultant

Prof. Terry Belanger
Columbia University

Roberto Brambilla
Institute for Environmental Action

Oscar A. Campa
*American Institute of Aeronautics
and Astronautics*

Dr. A. L. Carsten
Brookhaven National Laboratory

Lars Cederqvisit, M.D.
Gynecologist

Carroll Cline
Incorporated Consultants Ltd.

Paul Comer, M.D.
Anaesthesiologist

John Dalton
Modelworks Inc.

David Devaleria
Columbia University

Ken Distler
Ademco Inc.

David Dooling
Huntsville Alabama Times

Lt. Robert Donovan
U.S. Navy

Prof. Patricia Dudley
Barnard College

Prof. Rene Eastin
Long Island University

Prof. Rhodes Fairbridge
Columbia University

Prof. Gerald Feinberg
Columbia University

Robert Feitlowitz
Textiles consultant

Leonard Feldman
Leonard Feldman Electronic Lab.

John Fitch
Automotive consultant

Dr. Desmond A. Fitzpatrick
IBM

Sara Friedman
Botanical author

Michael Garvey, M.D.
Animal Medical Center

Prof. Allan Gilbert
Columbia University

Dr. John Gmeiner
Clinical psychiatrist

Eugene Grisanti
*International Flavors and
Fragrances, Inc.*

Annabelle Harris
International Paper Inc.

Kevin Hayes
Typesetter

Norman Hollyn
Film editor

Jonathan House, M.D.
Physician

Elizabeth Kellner
Nutritionist

Prof. Ellis Kolchin
Columbia University

Prof. Martin Kramer
City College of New York

T. Kuroiwa
Japan Smoking Articles Assoc., Tokyo

Prof. Charles Larmore
Columbia University

Warren Levin, M.D.
World Health Medical Group

Janet Loughridge
American Health Foundation

Dr. William Love
Brookhaven National Laboratory

Dr. John Maisey
American Museum of Natural History

Dr. James Macpherson
Engineering consultant

Eli Martin
Architect

Derrick McDowell
Earth sciences consultant

Elvin McDonald
Gardening consultant

Kenneth Meisler, M.D.
Preventive and Sports Medical Center

Jim Marchese
Photographer

Judith Molnar
Biologist

Dr. Peri Namerow
*Center for Population and
Family Health*

Lt. Joseph Nimmich
U.S. Coast Guard

Ruth Nussenzeig, M.D.
New York University Medical Center

Dom Perciballi
Emergency medical technician

Felix Peruggi
Fireworks by Grucci Inc.

Alice Petropoulos
National Council on Alcoholism

David Pope
Computer consultant

Walter Reed
National Automatic Merchandising Assoc.

Ronald Reider, M.D.
Psychiatrist

Robert Robertson
Oceaneering Inc.

James Rosenthal
Magnet Paint and Varnish Inc.

Andrew Salter, M.D.
Psychiatrist

Herbert Sander, M.D.
Preventive and Sports Medicine Center

J. E. Scherer
Liberty Studios Inc.

Dr. Ralph Shutt
Brookhaven National Laboratory

Prof. Philip Smith
Columbia University

Betty Sprigg
Pentagon, Washington

Timothy Steinhoff
Gardening consultant

D. William Strohemier
Arthur Schmidt and Assoc.

Dr. Joseph Thach
Pentagon, Washington

Peter Tischbein
U.S. Army Corps of Engineers

Joseph Trammell
Navesync Sound Inc.

Dr. Debra Triantafyllou
Mitre Inc.

K. C. Tung
*American Institute of Aeronautics
and Astronautics*

Prof. David Tyler
Columbia University

James Walkup
Psychology consultant

Prof. Walter Washko
University of Connecticut

Aura Weinstein
*American Institute of Aeronautics
and Astronautics*

Lillian Yung, E.D.D.
Columbia University

How to Use This Set

Science and Technology Illustrated contains 3,584 pages of colorfully illustrated, factually packed encyclopedic material. But the basic unit of the set is not the page but the article. There are 1,242 articles in this work.

The articles are arranged in alphabetical order, from ABACUS to ZIRCONIUM. An alphabetical arrangement has many advantages, and readers of encyclopedias generally prefer it.

The article ABACUS explains how to use this ancient calculating device that the Chinese and Japanese and some other peoples have employed for centuries. The article ZIRCONIUM explains the part that element plays in the great organization of matter that is described in the Table of Elements. It also tells what man knows about zirconium, and how he uses it.

In between are many, many other articles of the same kind, which explain how to use things, or what role things play in the overall structure of the universe, or what kind of a more general thing—a special animal, for instance—a particular thing is.

Science and Technology Illustrated also contains articles that deal with aspects of the world or things within the world, most notably with aspects of man. Human beings are unique in being able to communicate in spoken and written language; there is a wonderful article on LANGUAGE, what it is and how it works. Human beings are also unique in creating an organized system of knowledge with which they are able to investigate the world around them; there are also fine articles on many individual sciences.

Usually the best way to use *Science and Technology Illustrated* is to look at the Index first. The Index begins on page 3,552 in Volume 28. Look up the word or term in which you are especially interested, and then go to the article in the set to which the Index sends you.

Often, however, if what you are interested in is a particular species of plant or animal, or an element, or a tool or other device, or a scientific instrument, or a science or other means of knowing, you can save time by turning directly to the volume in which the article dealing with your subject falls, in alphabetical order. The choice of article titles has been carefully made to assist the reader who desires to use the set in this way.

Many articles end with cross references to other articles. These send you to articles that cover similar subjects, or that deal with subjects that you should first understand before trying to understand the article you are reading. Usually it is a good plan to follow up these cross references.

The best way of all to use *Science and Technology Illustrated* is to read it and have fun with it, and let it stretch your mind and your imagination!

Science and Technology Illustrated
The World Around Us

Cancer
Candle
Canning and Preserving
Cantilever
Capacitors and Resistors
Carbohydrates
Carbon
Carbon Dating
Carboniferous Period
Carburator and Injector
Card Games
Cardiology
Cartography
Cash Machine
Cash Register
Casting and Molding
CAT
CAT Scanner
Catalyst and Catalysis
Cathode Ray Tube
Cattle
Cave
Cell
Cement
Cenozoic Era
Central Heating
Central Processing Unit
  (CPU)
Centrifugal and Centripetal
  Force
Centrifuge
Ceramics
Cereal
Cermets
Chain Reaction
Character Recognition,
  Optical
Chart, Marine
Checkers
Cheese

VOLUME 6

Chemical Analysis
Chemical Bond and Valence
Chemical Element
Chemical Plant
Chemical Reaction
Chemical Warfare
Chemistry
Chemistry, Industrial
Chemistry, Organic
Chess
Chicken Pox

Childhood and Early
  Development
Chlorine
Chlorophyll
Chocolate
Cholera
Cholesterol
Chordata
Chromatography
Chromium and Molybdenum
Chromosome
Circuit, Electric
Circuit, Electronic
Circuit, Integrated
Circuit, Logical
Circuit Breaker
Circulatory System
Climate
Climate History
Clinical Analysis
Clocks and Watches
Clothing Manufacture
Cloud
Cloud Chamber
Clutch and Gearbox
Coal
Coal Gas
Coasts
Coaxial Cable and
  Waveguide
Cobalt
Coffee
Coil
Coins and Minting
Cold, Common
Collections (Natural History)

VOLUME 7

Color
Comet
Communication
Communications, Military
Compass
Computer
Computer, Personal
Computer Animation
Computer Design
Computer Games
Computer Graphics
Computer Lanuages
Computer Memory
Computer Peripherals
Computer Programs

Computer Terminal
Conception
Concrete
Condensation
Conditioned Reflex
Constellation
Construction Site
Contact Lens
Continent
Continental Drift
Continental Shelf
Copper and Cooper Alloys
Coral Reef and Atoll
Corn (Maize)
Corrosion
Cortisone
Cosmetics
Cosmology
Cotton
Cranes and Lifting Devices
Credit Card
Cretaceous Period
Critical Mass
Crops
Crossbow
Cruiser
Cryogenics
Cryptography
Crystal and Crystallography

VOLUME 8

Cybernetics
Dairy Industry
Dam
Dance
Darkroom
Data Bank
Data Base
Data File
Data Processing
DDT and Other Insecticides
Death
Defoliant
Dentistry and Dental
  Hygiene
Deodorant
Depression
Depth Charge
Desalinization
Desert
Desertification
Detergent
Devonian Period

Diabetes
Dialysis
Diamond
Diesel Engine
Dietetics
Differential, Automobile
Diffraction
Digestion
Digestive System
Digital Readout
Dinosaur
Diode
Diphtheria
Disease
Disease, Communicable
Disease, Hereditary
Dishwasher
Disinfectant
Distillation
DNA and RNA
Dock
Dog
Dolphin
Doppler Effect
Dowsing
Drafting
Drainage
Drawing
Dredge

VOLUME 9

Drills
Drugs and Medicines
Dry Cleaning and Pressing
Duplicating and
  Photocopying
Dye
$E = mc^2$
Ear
Earth (Planet)
Earth, Core
Earth, Crust
Earth, Mantle
Earthquake
Echinoderm
Eclipse
Ecology and Ecosystems
Egg
Ejection Seat
Elastomers
Electric Blanket
Electric Mixer
Electric Motor

Electric Power
Electric Wiring
Electricity
Electrocardiograph
Electrochemistry
Electroencephalograph
Electrolysis
Electromagnetism
Electron Optics
Electronic Surveillance
Electronics
Electro-Optics
Electrophoresis
Elevator
Embryo and Embryology
Enameling
Encoder, Digital
Endocrine System
Endoscopy
Energy
Energy Conservation
Energy Production,
   Worldwide

VOLUME 10

Energy Sources
Energy Sources, Marine
Engineering
Entropy
Enzyme
Ergonomics
Erosion
Escalator
Etching and Engraving
Ethology
Ethylene and Polyethylene
Evolution
Evolutionary Convergence
Exercise and Physical
   Fitness
Expanding Universe
Explosives
Eye
Eyeglasses
Fallout Shelter
Fats
Faults and Folds
Female
Fermentation
Ferry
Fertilizer
Fever
Fiber Optics

Fibonacci Series
Fighter-Bomber
Fighter-Interceptor
Film Editing
Filter
Fire and Combustion
Firefighting
Fireplace
Fireworks and Flares
First Aid
Fish
Fish Farming
Fishing
Flashlight
Flight Control Mechanisms
Flower

VOLUME 11

Flu
Fluidics
Fluorescence
Fluorinated Polymers
Fog
Food
Food Additive
Food Preservation
   Temperature
Food Processing
Food Production Atlas
Food Resources, Marine
Food Vending Machine
Forage
Forces and Fields of Force
Forensic Medicine
Forest and Forestry
Forging
Fossil and Fossilization
Foundation
Foundation Pen
Freeze-Drying
Freon
Friction
Fruit
Fuel Cell
Fur and Fur Industry
Furnace
Furniture
Galaxy
Galvanization
Garage
Gardening
Gas
Gas Chromatography

Gas Compressor
Gas Discharge
Gas Mask
Gas Turbine
Gasoline (Petrol)
Gear
Geiger Counter
Gem
Gene
Genetic Engineering
Genetics

VOLUME 12

Geochemistry
Geodesy
Geoid
Geological Map
Geology
Geometry
Geomorphology
Geophysics
Geothermal Energy
Geyser
Glacier
Gland
Glass
Gliders and Sailplanes
Glycogen
Gold
Graft, Medical
Graft, Plant
Grassland
Gravity and Gravitation
Greenhouse
Greenhouse Effect
Grinding and Polishing
Ground, Electrical
Growth
Guitar
Gunpowder
Guns and Ammunition
Gynecology
Hair and Fur
Hair Dryer
Halogens
Handgun
Harbor
Headache
Hearing
Hearing Aid
Heart
Heart Attack
Heat

Heat Transfer
Heat Treatment
Heavy Water
Helicopter
Hemophilia
Hepatitis
Herbarium
Heredity

VOLUME 13

Herpes
Hertzsprung-Russel Diagram
Hibernation
High Fidelity
High-Tension Line
Histology
Holocene Epoch
Holography
Holography, Acoustical
Homeopathy
Honey
Hormone
Horn
Horse
Hospital
Hot-Air Balloon
Houseplants
Hovercraft
Human Body
Human-Powered Flight
Hunger
Hurricanes and Other Storms
Hybrid
Hydraulic Transmission
Hydraulic Turbine
Hydraulics
Hydrocarbon
Hydrofoil
Hydrogen
Hydroponics
Hygiene
Hyperdense Matter
Hypnosis
Hypocaust
Ice Ages
Ice Cream
Igneous Rock
Immunity
Industrial Control
Industrial (Prefabricated)
   Housing
Inertia
Inertial Navigation

Roads and Highways
Robot
Rock
Rocket and Rocket Engine
Rolling Mill
Root
Rope and Cable
Rotogravure
Rudder
Saccharine and Sweetening
    Agents
Safety Industrial
Safety System, Factory

VOLUME 23

Salt
Salts
Sandblasting
Satellite
Satellite, Hunter-Killer
Satellite, Reconnaissance
Satellite, Surveying
Saturn
Savanna
Saw
Scales and Weighing Devices
Science and Scientific
    Method
Scintillation Counter
Screw
Scuba Diving
Sedimentary Rock
Seed
Seismograph
Semiconductor
Sets and Set Theory
Sewage Treatment
Sewing Machine
Sex
Sextant
Shampoo
Shark
Sheep
Shellfish, Crustacean
Ship Models
Shipbuilding
Shipping
Shock
Shock Absorber
Shoemaking
Shore
Silencer
Silicone

Silicons
Silk
Silo
Silurian Period
Silver
Siren
Skin
Skis and Skiing
Skylab
Slide Projector
Slingshot Effect
Smallpox
Smart Bomb
Smell

VOLUME 24

Snow
Soap
Sociobiology
Sodium
Sodium Nitrate and Nitrite
Soft Drinks
Soil
Solar Energy
Solar Heating
Solar System
Solid State Physics
Solvent
Sonar
Sound
Sound Effect
Sound Track
Soundproofing
Soybean
Space Observatory
Space Probe
Space Shuttle
Spectral Class
Spectrophotometer
Spectroscopy
Spectrum
Speech
Speedometer
Spiders and Other
    Arthropods
Spinning
Spleen
Spores and Sporogenesis
Sports
Sports Medicine
Spring and Elasticity
Stained Glass
Star

Star Clusters
Star Map
Starvation
Statics
Statistics
Steam Engine
Steam Shovel
Steam Turbine
Steel

VOLUME 25

Steering, Automobile
Stegosaurus
Steppe and Tundra
Stereo
Stereochemistry
Stethoscope
Stimulant
Stomach
Stonecutting
Stonehenge
Strobe
Submarine
Subway and Streetcar
Sugar
Sulfur
Sun
Sundial
Superconductor
Superfluid
Supernova
Supersonic Aircraft
Supersonic Flight
Surface Tension
Surgery
Surveying
Swimming
Synthesizer
Synthetic Fibers and Fabrics
Synthetic Fuels
Tanks and Armored Vehicles
Tape Recorder
Taste
Taxidermy
Taximeter
Tea
Tectonics
Telegraph
Telematics
Telephone
Telephone Answering
    Machine
Telescope

Telescope, Amateur
Teletypewriter
Television
Telex
Temperature and
    Temperature Scales
Terpene
Tertiary Period

VOLUME 26

Testosterone
Tetanus
Textile
Thermal Expansion
Thermodynamics
Thermoelectricity
Thermography
Thermometer
Thermonuclear Fusion
Thermostat
Thorium
Threshing Machine
Thunderstorm
Thyroid
Tide
Tile
Time
Tin
Tire
Titanium
Titration
Toaster
Tobacco
Tokamak
Toluene and Xylene
Tool
Toothpaste
Topography
Topology
Tornado
Torpedoes and Mines
Touch
Toxicology
Tractor
Traffic Control
Transducer
Transfer Machine
Transformer
Transistor
Transport, Special and
    Heavy-Duty
Transuranium Elements
Trap

Volume 1

Contents

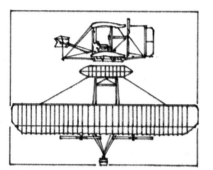

Abacus

The abacus is the most ancient calculating device known. Probably invented more than 5,000 years ago in Babylon, it has fallen into disuse in most of the world, although it is still widely used in Japan, where it is called a *soroban,* and in China, the Middle East, and the Soviet Union. It is also used in some schools as a teaching device for children just beginning arithmetic.

At the end of World War II, the Tokyo staff of *Stars and Stripes,* the U.S. Army newspaper, sponsored a contest between a Japanese *soroban* expert and an American soldier-accountant equipped with the best electric adding machine, as pre-electronic calculators were called. Both contestants were fed a steady stream of complex problems in addition, subtraction, multiplication, and division. To the surprise of the Americans, the Japanese expert proved to be clearly the faster operator except in the multiplication of very large numbers.

In its commonest form, the abacus consists of a rectangular frame crossed by (usually) nine rods or wires on which movable beads are strung. There is a bar running perpendicular to the rows of beads that separates them into two groups, one containing five beads, the other two. Each bead of the larger group counts as 1, each bead of the smaller group as 5. The nine rods or wires are the equivalent of columns of written figures—the first column on the right represents units, the others,

moving to the left, are for tens, hundreds, thousands, tens of thousands, and so on. (Some variations on the basic abacus design have five unit-beads on each wire, although four unit-beads and a single fives bead are sufficient, as on the commonest

Above: Diagram of the processes of addition and subtraction on the abacus. With four-digit numbers, as in the example, there are 10 separate steps, which an experienced operator performs almost simultaneously.

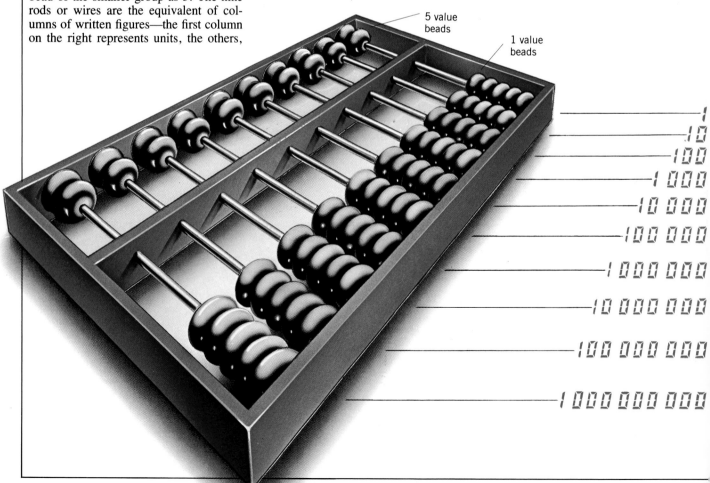

5 value beads

1 value beads

1
10
100
1 000
10 000
100 000
1 000 000
10 000 000
100 000 000
1 000 000 000

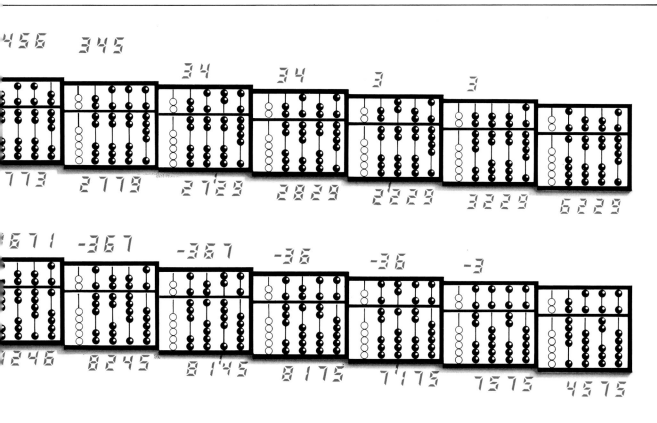

form of the *soroban*. A decimal version, with ten beads on each wire and without a crossbar, also exists.)

To begin working, the operator moves all beads to the outer edges of the frame. To enter the number 12,345, as an example, he moves one of the beads on the fifth wire from the right (the tens-of-thousands column) to the bar in the middle; this registers (1 × 10,000). Next, he moves two of the beads on the next wire to the middle to enter (2 × 1000). Three beads are moved to the center on the hundreds wire and four on the tens wire. On the units wire, the operator can use either the five beads on one side of the bar or a single bead of the "fives" side of the bar (remember that each bead of the pair is equal to five units; in the tens column, it would be equal to five tens, and so on). If we represent the beads by the letter x, the final array for 12,345 will look like this:

```
X X X X X X X X X X
X X X X X X X X X
                  X
              X X X X
X X X X   X X X X
X X X X X   X X X
X X X X X X   X X
X X X X X X X   X
X X X X X X X X X
```

The column values here are:
0 0 0 0 0 1 2 3 4 5

If to the above figure the operator wishes to add, say, 23,456, he will change the setting of the abacus as follows:

Mentally add 5 + 6 = 11, enter 1 in the units column by restoring the five-counter to its original position while shifting a one-counter to the bar; carry 1 to the tens column by shifting the four single counters to their "home" position and moving one five-counter to the bar. Adding 5 (from the number 23,456) to this equals 10, so the tens column is now to register 0 with 1 to carry. The operator continues in this way (in far less time than it takes to tell), and after a few lightning flicks of his fingers, the array is recast in the form giving the total:

```
X X X X X X X X X X
X X X X X X       X X
              X X
─────────────────────
          X   X   X
X X X X X X   X X
X X X X X X   X X X
X X X X X     X X
X X X X X   X X X X
X X X X X   X X X X
```

0 0 0 0 0 3 5 8 0 1

From the above it becomes clear that the abacus is more a notational instrument than a calculating machine. That is, the calculating is still done by the operator, who simply uses the abacus to keep track of his work.

The systems of written numerals used by the ancient Greeks and Romans were extremely clumsy. Both used letters of the alphabet in different ways to indicate numbers, and the use of the zero was unknown to them. It was only when an early 13th-century Italian merchant with a gift for figures, Leonardo Fibonacci (also known as Leonardo of Pisa), traveled to the Arab world that the Hindu discovery of the zero became known to Europeans. With the advent of the zero and Arabic number notation, addition, subtraction, multiplication, and division became simpler; there was less need of the abacus as a crutch, and its use gradually diminished, especially in Europe. It was still fairly common up to the 17th century, and, as mentioned above, its use has persisted in parts of the Middle East and Far East. To the extent that electronic computing aids become available in these areas, the use of the abacus will doubtless further decline.

Humble, outdated, and perhaps destined to become extinct except as a museum piece, the abacus has been, for well over 50 centuries, the only widespread mechanical calculating aid. It was not until the 17th century that Blaise Pascal, a French mathematician and philosopher of genius, made the first great advance over the abacus with his invention of a calculating machine using cogged wheels, which worked much as the familiar automobile speedometer does today.
See COMPUTER.

Accordion

Tango, polka, Cajun folk music, and jazz are all styles of music played on the accordion, a portable wind instrument incorporating a bellows that forces air through sounding reeds. The accordion is a fairly modern instrument; it was invented in 1822 by Friedrich Buschmann of Berlin, who called it a *Handäoline*. The instrument was improved in 1828 by Cyril Demian of Vienna, who gave it the name *Akkordion*.

The accordion belongs to a family known as the free-reed instruments. The other free-reed instruments are the harmonica, harmonium, and concertina. They were also developed in the early 1800s. The free reed is a thin strip of metal (originally brass) secured at one end above an opening of the same dimensions as the reed. When air flows past the reed, it is set into a vibratory motion, resembling that of a leaf spring, whose frequency, or the musical "pitch" that is heard, is proportional to the size of the reed.

In an accordion, pairs of reeds face opposite directions, and each pair is made to sound by a single keyboard-actuated air valve, so that a note will sound both when the bellows is compressed (forcing air out) and when it is expanded (drawing air in). These double-direction reeds are arranged in two oblong wood housings on either side of the large bellows. On top of the housings are the keyboard-actuated valves that open to admit air to a reed (single, melodic note) or group of reeds (chord). In a harmonica, the free reeds are arranged in a metal casing so that they can be blown into directly from the mouth. The harmonium is a type of organ fitted with free reeds, a keyboard, and air supplied by a foot bellows or, more recently, by an electric fan. The concertina is similar to the accordion. It has a bellows in the middle, and at each end, buttons activate the reeds. The sides of the concertina are octagonal in shape rather than rectangular, the buttons are arranged in a circle, and its range of notes is smaller.

Elaboration of the Handäoline

The first accordions were much different in design from the accordions built today. Brass was originally used for the free reeds, but in the 1850s, steel was substituted because it creates a steady, unwavering pitch. Another innovation was the replacement of the original column of levers along the right side with a piano-style keyboard. (The modern accordion has a piano keyboard on the right side and rows of buttons that activate accompanying chords and bass notes on the left.) A further refinement in the 1900s was the addition of registers (similar to organ stops) to both sides of the accordion. One register level, for example, would bring into play in unison a set of reeds one octave above the melody being played. There are also a lower-octave unison register and two "tremolant" registers. These levers activate sets of reeds that, when played in slightly mistuned unison with the main melody keys, create interferences in the sound waves that are audible as "beats," or loudness fluctuations, of some six cycles per second. (The same effect is created in the tremolo harmonica.)

Performance

Before the development of the modern piano-style accordion, the concertina was

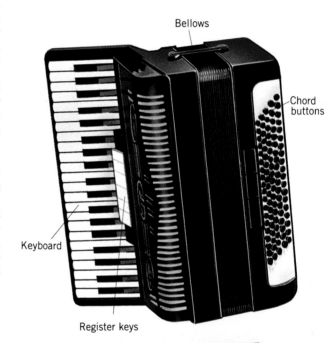

Bellows

Chord buttons

Keyboard

Register keys

The heart of the accordion is a bellows, which produces the flow of air necessary to make sound. The various keyboards (piano-style, register, and chord buttons) route this flow to different combinations of reeds, determining different notes and chords.

The photo on the left shows an early-19th-century forerunner of the modern accordion.

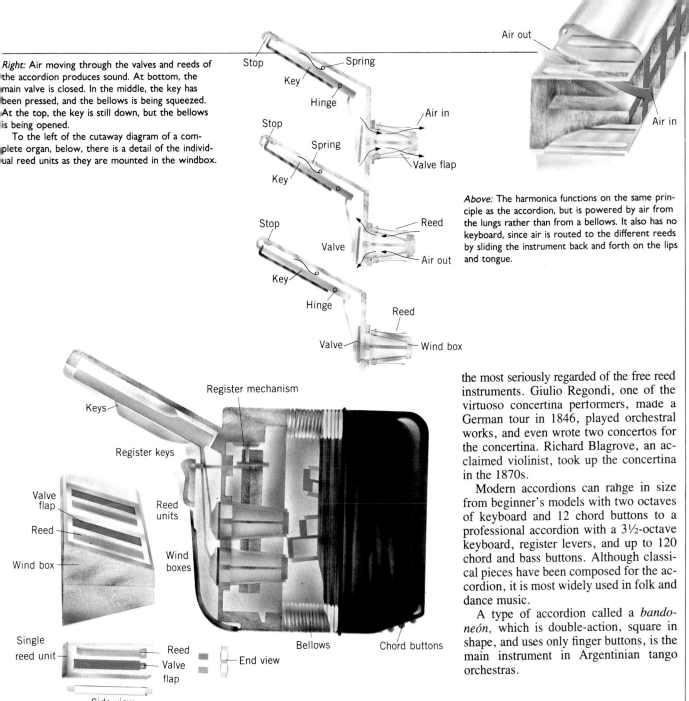

Right: Air moving through the valves and reeds of the accordion produces sound. At bottom, the main valve is closed. In the middle, the key has been pressed, and the bellows is being squeezed. At the top, the key is still down, but the bellows is being opened.

To the left of the cutaway diagram of a complete organ, below, there is a detail of the individual reed units as they are mounted in the windbox.

Air out

Air in

Stop
Spring
Key
Hinge

Stop
Spring
Key
Air in
Valve flap

Stop
Reed
Valve
Key
Air out

Hinge
Reed
Valve
Wind box

Above: The harmonica functions on the same principle as the accordion, but is powered by air from the lungs rather than from a bellows. It also has no keyboard, since air is routed to the different reeds by sliding the instrument back and forth on the lips and tongue.

Register mechanism
Keys
Register keys
Valve flap
Reed
Wind box
Reed units
Wind boxes

Single reed unit
Reed
Valve flap
End view
Side view

Bellows
Chord buttons

the most seriously regarded of the free reed instruments. Giulio Regondi, one of the virtuoso concertina performers, made a German tour in 1846, played orchestral works, and even wrote two concertos for the concertina. Richard Blagrove, an acclaimed violinist, took up the concertina in the 1870s.

Modern accordions can range in size from beginner's models with two octaves of keyboard and 12 chord buttons to a professional accordion with a 3½-octave keyboard, register levers, and up to 120 chord and bass buttons. Although classical pieces have been composed for the accordion, it is most widely used in folk and dance music.

A type of accordion called a *bandoneón,* which is double-action, square in shape, and uses only finger buttons, is the main instrument in Argentinian tango orchestras.

Accounting, Computerized

Accounting may have begun when the first transaction was recorded by some primitive entrepreneur. But while a preserved record, whether notched on a stick or written in a carefully maintained ledger, is an essential part of the accounting function, it is only the beginning. Keeping records of transactions such as sales, inventory, and employee hours is a necessary bookkeeping function, but accounting goes beyond that, using financial data about an organization to plan for the future. To this end, all data generated to record transactions are relevant. However, this information has to be evaluated in terms of the general context—such as political and economic conditions, prospects of recession, technological innovations, new tax laws, and the like.

There are no fixed limits to the legitimate concerns of accountants in the performance of their work. However, there are various specialties, such as financial accounting, cost accounting (establishing the actual cost of the various activities or

would turn to computers to satisfy these needs.

Computerized Accounting

The use of computer-processed data is a natural way to facilitate the accountant's work. The amount of data is too great to be processed—or analyzed—by hand. In most large organizations, the data would be computerized even if there were no accountants, but normally the accountants are consulted when the system is designed, and there they can make the best use of their time by deciding the nature, form, and content of the reports and analyses they will require, and then letting the machines do the work of collecting and displaying the results. Accountants can help determine the methods to be used for getting the raw data into the system. Forms, records, and procedures to be followed in handling transactions are the basis of every accounting system.

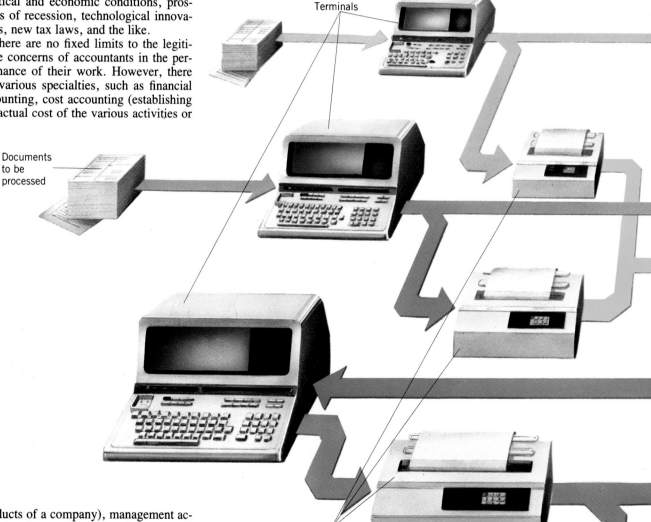

For accounting purposes, when extreme accuracy is necessary, terminals are sometimes tied directly to small printers, so that a paper copy of the input is immediately available to be checked against the original.

Terminals

Documents to be processed

Printers

products of a company), management accounting (evaluating past performance and predicting the effect of new policies), tax accounting, budgetary accounting, not-for-profit accounting (for government operations, foundations, and religious, educational, and charitable institutions), and social accounting (a new field that tries to evaluate the social and environmental effects—the costs and benefits—of governmental and industrial activities). All these specialities have in common their dependence on reliable, sufficient, and readily available data, and so it is logical that they

Though needs vary according to the size and structure of the company using the system computerized accounting requires a selection of hardware to acquire and process data and finally to put this information into a form that can be read by a human being from a cathode ray tube or a print out.

Data enters the accounting system—is input—by way of the terminals, but it can be output in a variety of ways: statistical tables or graphs, hard copy, an image on a CRT screen; or it can be passed directly to the computer's memory units.

For accounting purposes, when extreme accuracy is necessary, terminals are sometimes tied directly to small printers, so that a paper copy of the input is immediately available to be checked against the original.

Forms include sales invoices, vouchers, bank checks, and time cards—the immediate physical evidence of the activity.

Records include ledgers, journals, registers, and other means for compiling data.

Procedures are the general methods and rules established for handling the forms and records.

The data can be processed to produce not only payroll checks, purchase orders, bills, etc., but also various kinds of reports. These may be financial statements or any number of other statements and analyses based on the accounting data, which can be of use to management, the government, potential investors, owners, and various corporate departments (manufacturing, shipping, financial planning, etc.) to help them decide future actions. Programs exist that will generate reports tailored to a department's needs, according to certain multiple-choice options selected by the user. These are called Report Program Generators. Many other kinds of ready-made program packages are offered by computer manufacturers as well as by companies that produce nothing but specialized computer programs.

Some of the hardware and associated materials used in computerizing accounting are listed here. They include input media such as computer-readable optical and magnetic-ink characters on documents (such as checks), punched cards, and punched paper tape. Magnetic tape and magnetic disks are used to keep large volumes of data in more compact and quickly accessible form for the computer. Optical and magnetic-ink character documents can be machine processed and used for payroll and dividend checks and utility bills. They require processing equipment: a magnetic-ink character reader, optical character reader, a card reader, and card punch or keypunch to produce the cards. Other card-handling equipment includes a sorter, reproducer, collator, and tabulator. (All these devices are generally categorized as computer peripheral equipment.) Electronic computers have made some of the punched-card equipment obsolete, though some remains very much in use.

Applications include accounts receivable (the file of unpaid bills), perpetual inventories—which keep track of the supply of inventory items on a continuing basis, as distinguished from a physical inventory, which is not usually performed more than once a year—and payrolls. In a well-designed system, these and other functions are performed using data that are gathered routinely. Specialized artificial "languages" have been developed to help convey the user's needs to the computer.

What is most interesting and challenging from the viewpoint of the accountant and manager is the possibility of obtaining any desired information from a properly designed, integrated data-processing system, which not only will automatically do all the required processing but also can be easily adapted to accommodate new uses of the same data. Real-time processing is the term used to describe the continuous updating of records as the events occur. This generally also implies the possibility of accessing records as they are needed—by a customer who calls with a question about his bill, for example. The goal of all this is to arrive at an integrated management-information system, in which the data can be used to generate any desired set of reports for management, and new types of reports can be easily requested and produced.

See also COMPUTER; DATA PROCESSING.

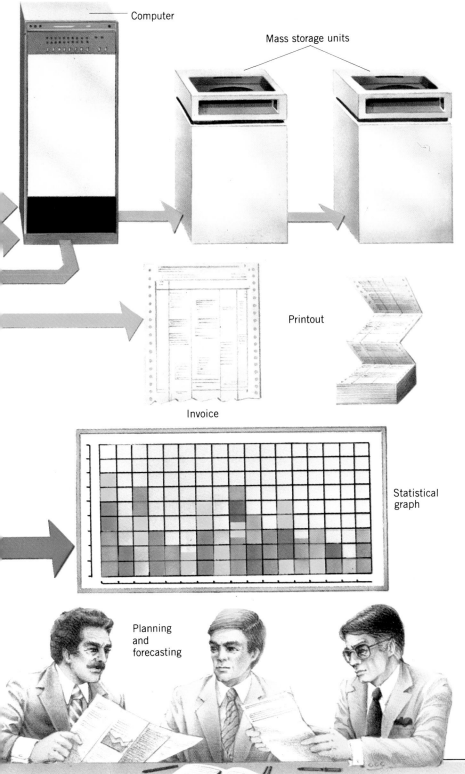

Computer

Mass storage units

Printout

Invoice

Statistical graph

Planning and forecasting

Acids and Bases

When Hannibal crossed the Alps to attack Rome in about 300 B.C., his troops carried casks of water mixed with vinegar to prevent the water from freezing in the icy passes. He did not know why vinegar was sour to the taste, nor that it was really a diluted form of acetic acid. All he knew was that vinegar didn't turn to ice as readily as water and that when wine went bad, vinegar was the result. From that time until the 20th century, acids were so incompletely understood that scientists did not even know how to define them.

In the past, acids were known under names as various as oil of vitriol (sulfuric acid) and spirit of salt (hydrochloric acid). Some are easily recognized; a few drops of strong acid rapidly eat their way through substances ranging from pieces of metal to unwary fingers. In fact, sulfuric and hydrochloric acid are so corrosive that the understanding of both was delayed for centuries by early researchers' inability to prevent them from destroying the apparatus in which they were made. After the Middle Ages, people learned to manipulate the power of acids so carefully that artists like Rembrandt used acid to etch

Acids can be represented by the general formula AH, in which H is a hydrogen atom that dissociates in water to form H^+ ions. A represents the rest of the molecule. Bases can be represented by the formula BOH, in which OH is a hydroxide that dissociates in water to form OH^- ions. B represents the rest of the molecule.

(H) — (A)		ACID
H — Cl		Hydrochloric acid
H — O, S	O, O	Sulfuric acid
H — O — N	O, O	Nitric acid
H — O, C — CH₃	O	Acetic acid

metal for beautiful engravings. Now, acids are also often used as catalysts—substances that make chemical reactions take place faster—in many industrial processes.

Acids have other qualities as well. Often they taste sour, as the German word for acid, *Saure*, indicates. Certain types of dye change color when acids are added to them. When acid is placed on a piece of chalk, carbon dioxide gas bubbles up. Last and most important, certain soapy-feeling substances called bases have the power to neutralize acids, and in the process they often form salts.

Medieval alchemists were able to discover the common mineral acids: nitric, sulfuric, hydrochloric, and phosphoric acids. They also learned that ammonia, baking soda (sodium bicarbonate), and calcium carbonate (the main component of limestone) served as bases. When various combinations of a common acid and a base were mixed together, the salts they produced included ordinary table salt (sodium chloride), saltpeter (potassium nitrate), and borax (sodium borate).

The Hydrogen Atom

Ancient scientists did not understand the acids they found because they had no way of knowing that all of them contain hydrogen, a very special element. Hydrogen is the lightest and most common of the more than a hundred chemical elements that make up the Universe. Like all other atoms, hydrogen atoms consist of a central nucleus surrounded by minute particles called electrons. The hydrogen nucleus is made up of a single positively charged particle called a proton; this is orbited by one negatively charged particle, an electron. All other atoms have more, and usually many more, than these two components.

Atoms of many varieties can sometimes lose or gain one or more of their electrons. (Except in extremely special circumstances, the nucleus never changes.) When they do so, the resulting, slightly different atom is known as an ion. Oxygen, for instance, usually picks up two extra electrons; when an oxygen atom does this, its ion is written as O^{--} or, more commonly, O^{2-}.

The single electron whirling about the hydrogen nucleus is easily stripped away, leaving an ion written as H^+. The plus sign means an atom has lost electrons, not

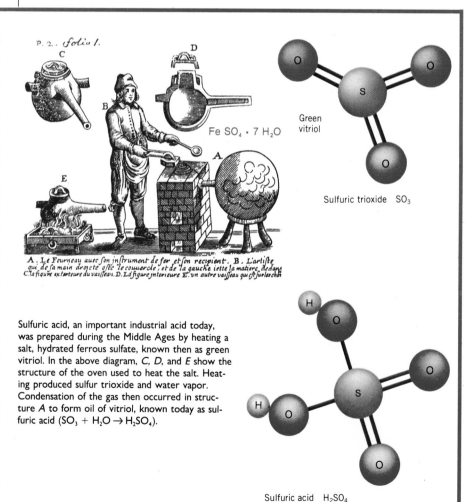

Sulfuric acid, an important industrial acid today, was prepared during the Middle Ages by heating a salt, hydrated ferrous sulfate, known then as green vitriol. In the above diagram, *C*, *D*, and *E* show the structure of the oven used to heat the salt. Heating produced sulfur trioxide and water vapor. Condensation of the gas then occurred in structure *A* to form oil of vitriol, known today as sulfuric acid ($SO_3 + H_2O \rightarrow H_2SO_4$).

Green vitriol

$Fe\,SO_4 \cdot 7\,H_2O$

Sulfuric trioxide SO_3

Sulfuric acid H_2SO_4

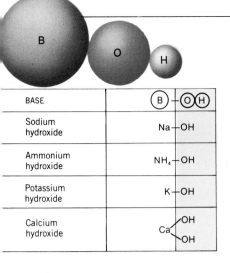

BASE		B —(O)(H)
Sodium hydroxide		Na—OH
Ammonium hydroxide		NH_4—OH
Potassium hydroxide		K—OH
Calcium hydroxide		Ca⟨OH OH

gained protons; the minus sign means an atom has acquired electrons, not shed protons. Unlike any other ion, H^+ consists only of a single lonely proton. For this reason, it is no more than about 10^{-14} centimeter in diameter, less than a millionth of a millionth of an inch.

Protons by themselves are so small that scientists think they are practically never found in a free state but are attached to much larger molecules. In 1923, Danish chemist Johannes Brønsted and English chemist Thomas M. Lowry almost simultaneously used this idea to explain acid-base reactions. They proposed that acids

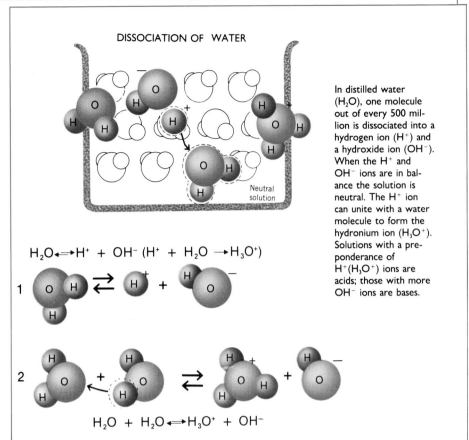

DISSOCIATION OF WATER

In distilled water (H_2O), one molecule out of every 500 million is dissociated into a hydrogen ion (H^+) and a hydroxide ion (OH^-). When the H^+ and OH^- ions are in balance the solution is neutral. The H^+ ion can unite with a water molecule to form the hydronium ion (H_3O^+). Solutions with a preponderance of H^+(H_3O^+) ions are acids; those with more OH^- ions are bases.

$H_2O \rightleftharpoons H^+ + OH^- (H^+ + H_2O \rightarrow H_3O^+)$

1

2

$H_2O + H_2O \rightleftharpoons H_3O^+ + OH^-$

The addition of an acid to water forms a solution containing an excess of hydronium ions released from the dissociation of the acid. The addition of a base to water forms an alkaline solution containing an excess of hydroxide ions formed from the dissociation of the base. The acidity, alkalinity, or neutrality of a solution can be determined by the addition of an indicator that changes color according to the degree of acidity or alkalinity. One of the most common is phenolphthalein. Another method is the use of litmus paper, which turns blue in bases and red in acids. The pH scale is a measure of acidity/alkalinity.

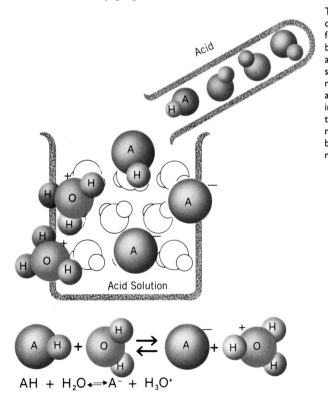

Acid

Acid Solution

$AH + H_2O \rightleftharpoons A^- + H_3O^+$

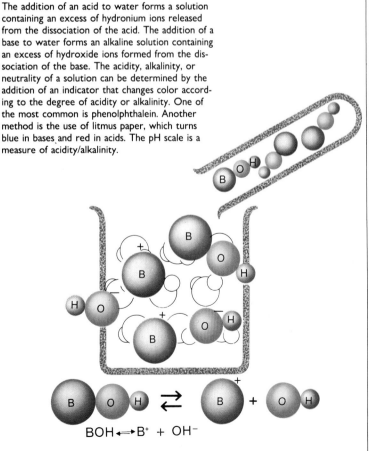

$BOH \rightleftharpoons B^+ + OH^-$

are made of molecules that give up H^+ ions and that bases are made of molecules that can accept them. All acid-base interactions, they said, are really just the passing of single hydrogen protons from the former to the latter. Chemically, strong acids seem to pass on their H^+ protons with the same urgency that football quarterbacks exhibit when they throw the ball under a heavy rush.

Brønsted-Lowry Reactions

An example of how this proton motion works is the reaction of hydrochloric acid, (which, in a dilute form, is called muriatic acid and which can be used to remove stains from porcelain) and sodium hydroxide (household lye). When combined, the two produce a mixture of table salt and water. The hydrochloric acid molecule is described in chemical notation as HCl, which means that it is made up of one hydrogen atom and one chlorine atom. Our stomachs contain a dilute solution of HCl to help us digest food. Sodium hydroxide is NaOH, which indicates that it is composed, respectively, of sodium (its Latin name, *natrium*, is the source of the symbol), oxygen, and hydrogen. In solution with water, HCl dissolves to form H^+ and Cl^- ions; NaOH turns into Na^+ and OH^-. This separation is called ionization; many acids, like hydrochloric acid, only show their acidic qualities when they are ionized in a solution.

Individual positive and negative ions are attracted to each other, whereas ionic charges of the same sign repel each other. (To understand this fully, see ION.) Thus, the H^+ and the OH^- ions in our example join to form a single molecule of nonionized HOH, which is almost always written as H_2O, ordinary water. The remaining Na^+ and Cl^- form NaCl (sodium chloride), the chemical name for the common salt on your kitchen table. The entire reaction can be written in the form:

$$Na^+ + OH^- + H^+ + Cl^- = H_2O + NaCl$$

Actually, $Na^+ + Cl^-$ remain in ionized form in water. If you dried out the solution, a white crystalline powder would remain: NaCl, common salt.

Do not think, though, that you can mix HCl and NaOH and drink the salty result. Not all of the acid-base is consumed by the reaction, and the salt water can still contain dangerously active chemicals.

More complex versions of this kind of reaction take place in your body all the time, ranging from the way subtle electrochemical processes activate neurons within the brain to the way sodium bicarbonate neutralizes excess stomach acid after a big meal. The Brønsted-Lowry theory sug-

gests that what has really happened in this and all other acid-base reactions is that an H^+ proton in the acid has slipped over to join part of the base.

Acid Structure

One of the reasons for an acid's "willingness" to let go an H^+ proton or two is the way acids are built. Many acids are structured in the form of regular geometric shapes with hydrogen atoms sticking out at the corners. An example is sulfuric acid, which has the formula H_2SO_4. First produced by European alchemists in the 13th century, sulfuric acid was discov-

STRONG ACIDS AND BASES		
ACIDS AH		**BASES BOH**
$AH \rightarrow A^- + H^+$ $AH + H_2O \rightarrow A^- + H_3O^+$		$BOH \rightarrow B^+ + OH^-$
$HClO_4$	Perchloric acid	NaOH — Sodium hydroxide
HCl	Hydrochloric acid	KOH — Potassium hydroxide
H_2SO_4	Sulfuric acid	
HNO_3	Nitric acid	$Ca(OH)_2$ — Calcium hydroxide
HI	Hydroiodic acid	
HBr	Hydrobromic acid	$Ba(OH)_2$ — Barium hydroxide
		$Sr(OH)_2$ — Strontium hydroxide

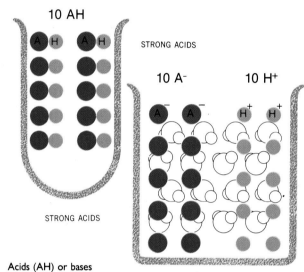

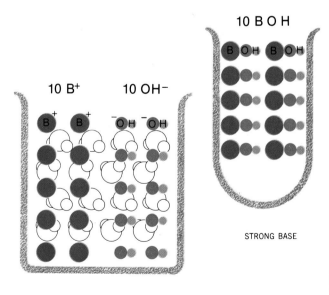

Acids (AH) or bases (BOH) dissociate in water to form ions. Acids form A^- ions and H^+ $(H_3O)^+$ ions, while bases form B^+ ions and OH^- ions. Strong acids and bases dissociate completely in water. For example, if 10 molecules of a strong acid are added to water, $10 H^+$ and $10 A^-$ ions form. If 10 molecules of a strong base are added to water, $10 B^+$ and $10 (OH)^-$ ions are formed.

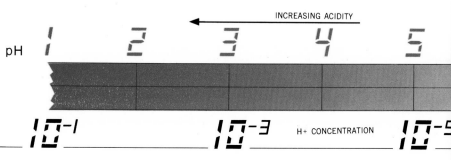

WEAK ACIDS AND BASES	
ACIDS AH	BASES BOH
A⁻ + H⁺ $H_2O \to A^- + H_3O^+$	$BOH \to B^+ + OH^-$
4 Phosphoric acid	NH_3 Ammonia
3 Carbonic acid	$[NH_3 + H_2O \to NH^+_4 +$
Hydrogen cyanide	$OH^-]$
Hydrosulfuric acid	$(CH_3)_3N$ Trimethylamine
3 Boric acid	$[(CH_3)_3N + H_2O \to$
Hydrofluoric acid	$(CH_3)_3NH^+ + OH^-]$
OOH Acetic acid	
)H Formic acid	

ered by haphazardly distilling mixtures of "vitriols" such as copper sulfate or of "alums" such as potassium aluminum sulfate. It was an important industrial chemical for centuries before people knew how it was put together on the molecular level. The molecule is shaped like a tetrahedron, with an oxygen atom in each of the four corners and a sulfur atom among them in the middle. From two of the four corners, however, hydrogen atoms stick out. These two H atoms—or, rather, their nuclei—can be easily separated from the rest of the structure, leaving their electron

behind with the O atom. The result is a regular tetrahedron-shaped SO_4^{2-} ion, the sulfate ion. Other tetrahedronal acids include phosphoric acid (H_3PO_4) and acetic acid ($HC_2H_3O_2$). (Like a few other acid formulas, $HC_2H_3O_2$ is written with an H in front to show that it has an easily detached hydrogen atom. Strictly speaking, $HC_2H_3O_2$ is only called acetic acid when it is in solution.)

Sulfuric acid can be dissolved in water to produce a strong acid solution. In water, the nuclei of the extra hydrogen atoms break off from the H_2SO_4 molecules, pro-

10 AH

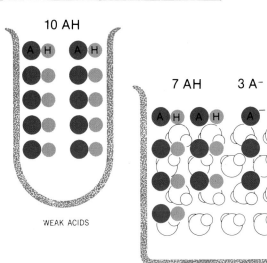

WEAK ACIDS

7 AH   3 A⁻   3 H⁺

Weak acids and bases undergo partial dissociation in solution. For example, if 10 molecules of a weak acid are added to water, only 3 A⁻ ions and 3 H⁺ ions form; the other 7 molecules do not dissociate. If 10 weak base molecules are added to water, 2 B⁺ ions and 2 OH⁻ ions form, while 8 molecules do not dissociate.

10 B O H

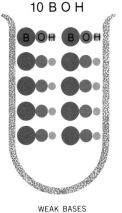

WEAK BASES

8 B O H   2 B⁺ 2OH⁻

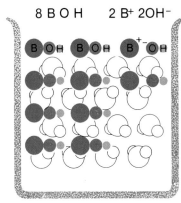

PH OF COMMON SUBSTANCES	
substance	pH
Hydrochloric acid (commercial concentration—37 percent by weight)	≈ — 1,1
1 M Hydrochloric acid	0,0
	1,4
Gastric juices	2,1
Lemon juice	2,8
Orange juice	3,5
Wine	4,1
Tomato juice	5,0
Espresso coffee	6,0
Urine	6,5
Rain water	6,9
Milk	7,0
Pure water at 75° F. (24° C.)	7,4
Blood	8,5
Baking soda solution	9,2
Borax solution	10,5
Limewater	11,9
Ammonia (domestic)	14,0
1M sodium hydroxide	≈ 15,0
Saturated sodium hydroxide	

The pH scale expresses the degree of concentration of hydrogen ions in a solution. The scale ranges from 0 to 15 and is mathematically related to the concentration of hydrogen ions. Water, with a concentration of H⁺ ions of 10^{-7}, has a pH of 7; this is the point of neutrality. Substances with a greater concentration of H⁺ have a lower pH and are acids, while those having a higher pH are bases.

$$* [H^+] \cdot [OH^-] = 10^{-14} \text{ g-ioni/l}$$

$$[H^+] = \frac{10^{-14}}{[OH^-]} \text{g-ioni/l} \qquad [OH^-] = \frac{10^{-14}}{[H^+]} \text{g-ioni/l}$$

*BRACKETS SIGNIFY "CONCENTRATION OF"

NEUTRALITY   INCREASING ALKALINITY →

7   8   9   10   11   12   13   14

10^{-7} 10^{-9} 10^{-11} 10^{-13}

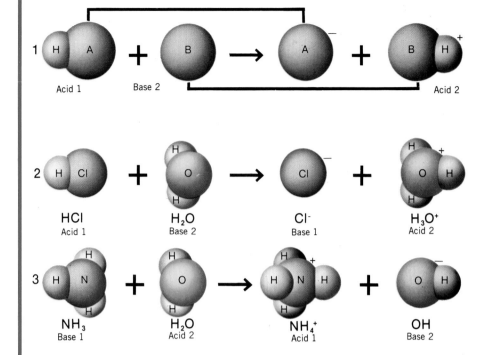

1. H A + B → A + B H (+)
   Acid 1   Base 2   Acid 2

2. H Cl + O H → Cl (−) + O H (+)
   HCl   H₂O   Cl⁻   H₃O⁺
   Acid 1   Base 2   Base 1   Acid 2

3. H N H + O H → H N H + O H (−)
   NH₃   H₂O   NH₄⁺   OH
   Base 1   Acid 2   Acid 1   Base 2

The Brønsted-Lowry theory defines acids as substances that donate H⁺ protons while bases accept H⁺ protons. Substances that are related through proton transfer are called conjugate acid base pairs. In diagram I, acid I donates a proton and becomes base I, while base 2 accepts a proton to become acid 2. In diagram 2, HCl and Cl⁻ are the conjugate acid base pair and water and H₃O⁺ are the other acid base pair. In diagram 3, water acts as an acid. Substances that can act either as an acid or a base, depending upon the reaction, are called amphiprotic.

ducing two H^+ ions for every SO_4^{2-} ion. If we drip some of this liquid onto a metal like zinc, the "greedy" protons will take electrons from the metal, becoming whole atoms again, and then the atoms will in turn combine into H_2 molecules, the form in which natural hydrogen most commonly occurs. Minus a few of its electrons, the metal becomes a positive ion that bonds with the negative sulfate ion, and in so doing it destroys its own structure and releases heat. A controlled version of this violent process is applied in making engravings and etchings, both of which use an acid solution to burn fine grooves into the metal plates of the printing press.

Acid-Base Pairs

In the sulfuric acid solution, SO_4^{2-} ions attract free H^+ protons—that is, they are acting just like bases. The relationship between sulfuric acid and its SO_4^{2-} ions is an example of one consequence of the Brønsted-Lowry definition of acids and bases. When acids ionize, the negative ions they generate are called conjugate bases; similarly, when bases accept protons, they become their own conjugate acids. The stronger the acid, the greater its tendency to lose a proton and the less likely is its conjugate base to accept back a proton. Strong acids, therefore, have weak conjugate bases, and weak acids have strong conjugate bases. Whether a

compound is an acid or a base at any given time depends on the position of its movable hydrogen protons.

On top of all this, some substances are both acids and bases. The most common example is water. H_2O can lose a proton to become a powerful base OH^-, which combines readily with H^+ to form water again. Water can also accept a proton to form H_3O^+, the hydronium or oxonium ion. Hydronium ions readily dump their extra proton, and so H_3O^+ is about as strong an acid as OH^- is a base. This dual, or amphoteric, quality of water is a major reason why so many acid-base interactions happen in water solutions.

Because of water's double identity as both an acid and a base, it is used as a chemical standard for acidity and alkalinity (or "baseness"). Pure water is the midpoint, roughly speaking, of the pH scale, which was invented by the Danish chemist S. P. L. Sørenson in 1909 to compare the strength of acid solutions. The pH scale is a measure of the number of hydrogen ions present in a solution. Normal pH values run from 0 to 14, with the pH of plain water being about 7.

When a solution has a pH lower than 7, it means that the amount of H^+ is higher than normal, and the solution is acidic. When it is higher than 7, there is less H^+ than usual, and the solution is alkaline. The pH value of a solution can be measured by a variety of chemicals that change

color according to the solution's acidity. These are known as indicators. One of the most common indicators is phenolphthalein, which is usually included in chemistry sets; it turns pink at about pH 8.5. Another well-known indicator, litmus paper, is a chemically treated paper that turns pink in acid and blue in base solutions.

Superacids

Some acids are so strong—that is, they can so easily donate protons—that they can't be measured on the pH scale. For example, although sulfuric acid solutions can be so strong that they have pH values of close to O, pure H_2SO^4 has an acidity approximately 10^{13} (ten million million) times greater than it does mixed with water. In fact, sulfuric acid with no water in it is potent enough to combine with salts and produce other, slightly weaker acids. When mixed with table salt, sulfuric acid produces powerful hydrochloric acid and $NaHSO_4$ (sodium hydrosulfate, another salt).

Pure sulfuric acid is so acidic that many materials that normally do not accept protons are forced into acid-base reactions with it. Among these are other acids like acetic acid, and ketones. For this reason, sulfuric acid, fluorosulfuric acid (HSO_3F, another extremely powerful acid), and others like them are often called superacids. These extremely dangerous chemicals are so hard to store that labs usually have them only in diluted form.

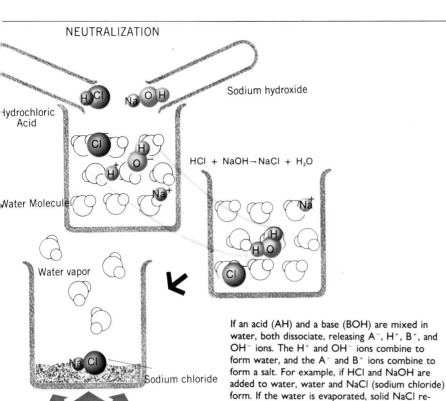

Sodium hydroxide

Hydrochloric Acid

Water Molecule

HCl + NaOH→NaCl + H₂O

$HCl + NaOH \rightarrow NaCl + H_2O$

Water vapor

Sodium chloride

If an acid (AH) and a base (BOH) are mixed in water, both dissociate, releasing A^-, H^+, B^+, and OH^- ions. The H^+ and OH^- ions combine to form water, and the A^- and B^+ ions combine to form a salt. For example, if HCl and NaOH are added to water, water and NaCl (sodium chloride) form. If the water is evaporated, solid NaCl remains.

Organic Acids

All the acids described thus far, except acetic acid, are mineral acids. But there are also many types of organic acids, that is, acids that contain carbon. (All carbon-containing compounds are called organic compounds, because chemicals of this type play such an important role in the life processes of animals and plants.) Organic acids are present in every cell in your body. They are found in substances ranging from candle wax to butter and nutmeg oil, and scientists are still exploring and discovering new ones all the time.

Most mineral or inorganic acids have simple formulas; hydrochloric acid, for instance, is simply HCl. Most organic acids, on the other hand, are chemical compounds of such complexity that the hydrogen atoms that give them their acid qualities tend to be overlooked. In fact, these acids are so complicated that even deciphering their names can be quite a trick. As an example, take CH_2OHCH_2-$CHBrCHBrCH_2COOH$, which, depending on the nomenclature system you use, is either 3,4-dibromo-6-hydroxyhexanoic acid or B2-dibromo-E-hydroxy-caproix acid.

Carboxylic Acids

Whatever name you use, CH_2OHCH_2-$CHBrCHBrCH_2COOH$ is one of a large class of organic acids called carboxylic acids. Carboxylic acids are the type of organic acids usually referred to when the term is used. They are so named because they all have a carboxyl group, a carbon atom bonded with a double bond to an oxygen atom and with a single bond to an OH molecule. The carboxyl group's formula is COOH, and all carboxylic acids have COOH at the end of their formulas. In organic chemistry, compounds are often diagrammed to represent their atomic structure. Carboxylic acids look like this:

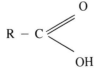

The H in the OH can drop off, which gives the carboxyl group its acidic properties. R stands for the rest of the acid molecule, and the dashes between the molecules indicate chemical bonds.

The simplest carboxylic acid, formic acid, is HCOOH. When a bee sting smarts or the bite of a red ant burns, it's because the formic acid in the bee's stinger or the ant's jaws has entered your bloodstream. The free hydrogen protons combine with compounds in your body, ripping chemical bonds and causing pain.

Another common carboxylic acid is acetic acid ($HC_2H_3O_2$), the active ingredient in wine vinegar. Organic chemists usually write this with the formula CH_3COOH. Like the other carboxylic acids, acetic acid reacts with metal to release hydrogen gas. With a variety of other chemicals, the carboxylic acids are used in textile manufacture.

A group of carboxylic acids called fatty acids are major components of the fat in animals and human beings and the oil in some plants. The most common, oleic acid, is present in palm, olive, peanut, and sunflower oils; another, stearic acid, comprises almost a third of animal lard.

Other Organic Acids

In addition to the more than 30 carboxylic acids, there are many other types of organic acids. One of these types, amino acids, is the essential stuff of proteins, substances that in turn are the basic constituents of our body cells. The 20 amino acids that make up proteins are only a few of the more than 200 amino acids that are known to exist. The arrangement of the special score of amino acids that make up proteins is in turn orchestrated by another set of acids, the nucleic acids DNA and RNA (deoxyribonucleic acid and ribonucleic acid). Unlike any other known chemical compounds, DNA and RNA can create replicas of themselves.

All of these are acids in the sense that they have the ability to pass on hydrogen protons. Yet, no chemist would say that an incredibly complicated substance like DNA was defined by its acidic qualities. Rather, they would say it is a complex molecule that happens to donate protons. This illustrates one problem with the Brønsted-Lowry definition, which is that it lumps together many different compounds under the same name. For this and other reasons, a number of alternate definitions have been proposed. Some of these are useful in certain circumstances, and all are still the subject of discussion by researchers.

In some ways, the argument over definition shows that despite all our knowledge, we are only a little closer to being able to put our finger on what we mean by "acid" than Hannibal was when he put acetic acid in his water casks.

See also ALDEHYDE AND KETONE; AMINES AND AMIDES; CARBON; CATALYST AND CATALYSIS; DNA AND RNA; ION; PH; PROTEIN.

Acoustics

A tree falls in the forest. Does it make a sound if no one is there to hear it? Amateur philosophers have pondered this question for years, but a straightforward answer is given by the elementary principles of acoustics—the study of the phenomenon of sound.

When a Sound Wave Makes a Sound

When a material, such as that tree in the forest, vibrates, a sound wave pushes out in all directions through surrounding solids, liquids, and gases. No matter how strong the vibrations, however, they cannot actually be said to make a sound unless they are intercepted by a special receiver such as your ears. Many sound waves are inaudible. You rarely hear ground or water sounds, for instance, because you spend little time with your ear to the ground or under the water. When you do hear sound, the process begins when the waves set up by the vibrations of a source (a guitar string, for instance) travel through a medium such as air into the ear canal and strike against the sensitive tympanic membrane of the eardrum. (For an account of the progress of the sound wave into the inner ear and then the brain, *see* HEARING AIDS.) The act of hearing requires a medium. Because none exists in the vacuum of outer space, sound is a phenomenon restricted to the atmospheric conditions of the Earth.

Sound Wave Media

Although many of the sound waves traveling through solids cannot be heard, that is where they travel the fastest, longest, and loudest. Stand back from a wall and rap it with your knuckles. You will hear those sound waves as they travel out from the wall and through the air. Now rap the wall again, but this time press your ear against it as you do. You will notice that the sound waves traveling inside the wall are louder. As a sound travels in an elastic medium, the molecules forming it are at first pushing together (condensation) and then pulling apart (rarefaction) more or less like an accordion. Condensation is responsible for the loudness of the sound. The denser the medium, the more intense the condensation of the wave. The wall you rapped with your knuckles is denser than the air, and therefore the sound you heard in the wall was louder than the sound you heard in the air. Sounds are louder in warm, humid air than in cold, dry air, louder still in water, and loudest in solids.

Although the range of a sound wave can be great, its energy is relatively small. A wave of normal loudness, such as a voice at a conversational level, contains about one millionth the energy required to light an ordinary light bulb. Despite this great difference in energy, a sound wave can be used to vary an electric current (for more information about this process, *see* MUSICAL INSTRUMENTS). With the advent of electric sound, the word "acoustic" began to be used in popular speech to describe any instrument with an electric counterpart. Hence, an "acoustic guitar" is simply a nonelectric guitar.

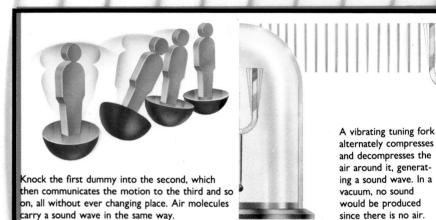

Knock the first dummy into the second, which then communicates the motion to the third and so on, all without ever changing place. Air molecules carry a sound wave in the same way.

A vibrating tuning fork alternately compresses and decompresses the air around it, generating a sound wave. In a vacuum, no sound would be produced since there is no air.

Sound Wave Travel

To understand the movement of the sound wave as it alternates between condensation and rarefaction, we can imagine what the air movement caused by the play of a guitar string looks like. As the string is plucked, it displaces the air molecules in front of it, crowding them into the molecules ahead. As the string bounces back, it leaves thin, rarefied air in its wake. The crowded, condensed air ahead, meanwhile, gets rid of its excess molecules by sending some backward into the rarefied air and by sending others forward, creating new condensation ahead. This condensation continues to ripple forward in waves of air molecules that become smaller and smaller the farther the wave travels from its source. For this reason, the farther the wave travels from its source, the weaker its sound.

The energy of a sound wave has the same back-and-forth motion as the molecules of the medium through which it is traveling. This may seem perfectly natural, but it is a distinctive characteristic of the longitudinal nature of sound-wave motion. Waves that you can see passing through water, for instance, are transverse. This type of wave disturbs the water molecules in an up-and-down direction, perpendicular to the wave itself.

Loudness and Pitch

The force of the original vibration of a sound wave determines the strength with which it strikes the eardrum and how loud it sounds. Loudness is measured in decibels, a unit whose meaning is best illustrated by the following table, which begins with the softest sound the human ear can hear and ranges upward to the loudest the ear can stand without intolerable pain.

This range is such that the loudest sound the ear can hear is one trillion times as loud as the softest.

The number of vibrations per second of

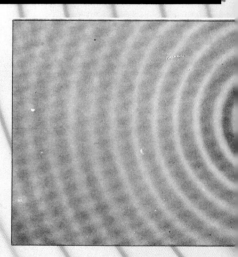

the sound wave is called the frequency, which corresponds to the pitch, or the "lowness" and "highness" of sounds. The lower the frequency of a sound wave, the lower the pitch, and the higher the frequency, the higher the pitch. Sound waves with frequencies outside the range of 20 to 20,000 vibrations per second are too low-pitched or too high-pitched for the human ear. Some animals are capable of hearing pitches outside this range, which accounts for the mysterious "silent whistle" used for calling dogs.

The pitch of a sound wave changes as the position of the sound source changes with respect to the listener. As a train rushes toward you, the sound of its wheels on the track changes from a low roar to a high scream. As the train comes closer to

Intensity of Sound

Type of Noise	Units	Decibels
Airplane engine nearby	1,000,000,000,000	120
	100,000,000,000	110
Airplane cabin (normal flight)	10,000,000,000	100
Heavy traffic, pneumatic drill	1,000,000,000	90
	100,000,000	80
Noisy office, telephone conversation, ordinary traffic	10,000,000	70
	1,000,000	60
Average office	100,000	50
Ordinary conversation	10,000	40
Quiet home, quiet conversation	1,000	30
	100	20
Rustle of leaves, whisper	10	10
	1	0

In *A*, above, wave amplitude is the distance between *a* and *b*; *c* to *d* is one cycle. The number of cycles per second is the frequency.

B is a diagram of two sounds of different intensity. Sound intensity depends on the amplitude of the wave.

C shows two sounds of different frequency. The more cycles there are per second, the higher the tone.

you, the sound waves are reaching you more rapidly, so the pitch is higher. The phenomenon of changes in pitch as the source comes toward the listener or recedes from him is called the *Doppler effect*.

Reverberations and Echoes

Out in open or free space, sound waves travel approximately 1,100 feet (335 m) per second (which technically is known as a speed of Mach 1). The intensity of these waves decreases by about one-third with each doubling of the distance between the sound source and the receiver. Much of the sound you hear, however, does not come directly from its source but bounces off reflective materials. These are dense, nonporous materials such as metals, plastics, and hard woods. Sound reflected off such surfaces is called reverberation. Reverberation is measured by the number of seconds or fractions of seconds it takes a particular wave to lose 60 decibels of sound after the original vibration causing the sound stops.

A room with few reverberant surfaces has a short reverberation time. In this type of room, sound comes directly from sound waves and very quick reflections. The location of the source can be easily identified. Reverberations reaching the receiver within 30 milliseconds tend to improve the clarity of sound and are desirable for understanding speech. If a sound travels more than 30 feet (9 m) before reflecting, reverberation occurs more than 30 milliseconds later. This delay tends to saturate the new sound waves being generated, and a distorted sound can result. When reverberations are delayed by more than 70 milliseconds, they separate entirely from

SPEED OF SOUND IN DIFFERENT SUBSTANCES

Solid
13,000–16,500 feet
(4,000–5,000 m)
per second

Liquid
5,000 feet
(1,500 m) per second

Gas
1,100 feet
(335 m) per second

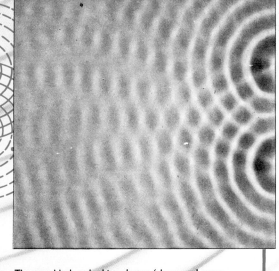

The two black-and-white photos (above and opposite page) show how waves spread in water, a model of how sound moves in the air. In the picture above, two sound waves interfere, partially canceling one another.

the original sound and are heard independently as echoes.

The best way to get rid of unwanted reverberations and echoes is with sound-absorbent materials, porous or resilient materials such as cloth and rubber. When sound waves move against curtains or rugs, they disperse into the pores of the fabric and dissipate their energy as heat instead of movement. Rubber interrupts the conduction of sound waves between objects. A rubber backing on a wall telephone, for instance, will absorb the vibration of the telephone bell and prevent the sound from being conducted into the wall. This absorption greatly diminishes the ringing of the telephone in a neighboring room.

Although echoes and delayed reverberations are not desirable in areas where speeches are given, they are integral to musical acoustics, and the desire for them greatly affects the architectural design of music halls.

Acoustical Architecture

The behavior of sound waves within buildings is one of the most important subjects of acoustics. Someone who asks, "How are the acoustics?" wants to know how sound carries throughout the room. But he may be asking this question with very different interests in mind. On the one hand, if he refers to a restaurant or office space, he is interested in whether sound remains localized in order to provide privacy. On the other hand, if he is asking about a performance area such as a theater or concert hall, he is interested in how sound travels throughout the room. The ability of a sound to travel and be clearly heard or to remain confined depends on the loudness of the original sound, other sounds occupying the same area, the shape and structure of the space, and the materials used in its construction.

Although some of the oldest structures in which performances were held—the

following its completion in 1962, the interior was remodeled, with further alterations made in 1964, 1965, 1969, and 1972. In 1973, the name of the hall was changed from the New York Philharmonic to Avery Fisher Hall in honor of the principal benefactor of the reconstruction projects. Finally, in 1976, the inside was entirely gutted and rebuilt, and this time the rebuilding was deemed a success.

What made the sound in the old Philharmonic Hall unpopular? And why are listeners happy with the new hall?

Among the complaints against the old auditorium were that the sound did not carry to the back of the auditorium and that it suffered from hot and dead spots, where it was either disagreably loud or weak. In a word, the sound was lifeless.

The new Avery Fisher Hall design livened things up in a number of ways. The curved back and side walls were replaced with heavy, flat, wood-paneled walls that

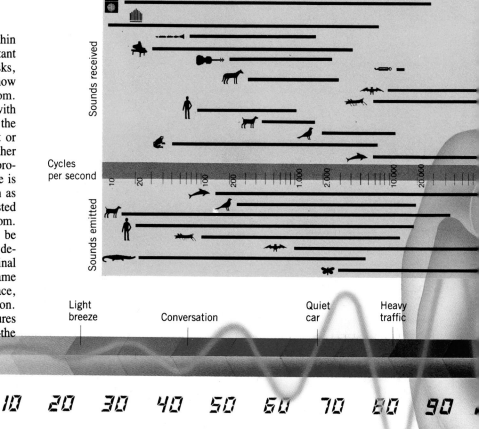

The ceiling is considered the most im portant reflective surface of a room be cause waves reflected off the ceiling reac every part of the room below. Anothe important function of the ceiling is to blen sounds together. A good ceiling for a mu sic hall should "grate" the sound wave mix them together, and send them out i all directions.

The old ceiling of Avery Fisher Ha was flat and too lightweight to diffus sound adequately. The new ceiling i made of heavyweight plaster capable o reflecting waves of all frequencies. Lik choppy ice on a river, its surface present different-sized planes jutting out at differ ent angles in different directions. This sur face diffuses sound waves well an distributes them in a pleasing blen throughout the large room. Because of th shallowness of the three tiers of balconie at the sides and back of the hall, every sea

Greek amphitheaters—achieved superb acoustical conditions, modern architects and acoustical engineers are still struggling with the problems of acoustics. The history of Avery Fisher Hall at Lincoln Center for the Performing Arts in New York is a good example. The express purpose of constructing the hall was to create an excellent acoustical setting for symphony concerts. Despite careful and expert planning, however, the building fell entirely short of its promise. The summer

give the hall a classic rectangular shape. While the old curved surfaces focused sound waves in centralized hot spots and deprived other spots of sound, the new walls broke up the sound and reflected it evenly throughout the room. The heavy oak panels enhanced the diffusion— breaking up the waves responsible for uniform sound distribution—because they were far less absorbent than the old walls, which were blamed particularly for absorbing low-frequency sound waves.

on the main floor catches reverberation from the ceiling.

The concrete floor of the old hall faile to conduct the vibrations of the musi through the floor and into the seats. Th new floor, made of thick oak, carries vi brations that the audience can feel throug the soles of their feet and their chairs.

The acoustical merits of one place, how ever, may be the bane of another. Aver Fisher Hall was specifically designed as hospitable environment for symphonies

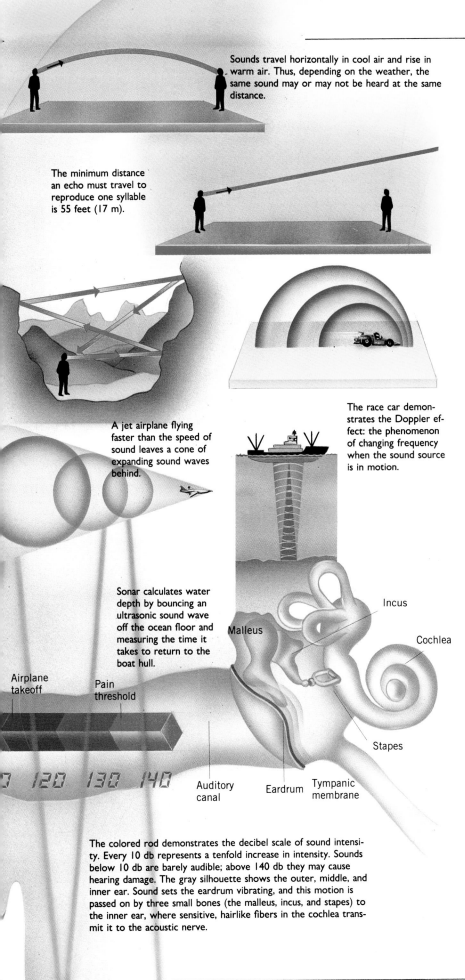

Sounds travel horizontally in cool air and rise in warm air. Thus, depending on the weather, the same sound may or may not be heard at the same distance.

The minimum distance an echo must travel to reproduce one syllable is 55 feet (17 m).

A jet airplane flying faster than the speed of sound leaves a cone of expanding sound waves behind.

The race car demonstrates the Doppler effect: the phenomenon of changing frequency when the sound source is in motion.

Sonar calculates water depth by bouncing an ultrasonic sound wave off the ocean floor and measuring the time it takes to return to the boat hull.

Incus

Cochlea

Malleus

Stapes

Airplane takeoff

Pain threshold

0 120 130 140

Auditory canal

Eardrum

Tympanic membrane

The colored rod demonstrates the decibel scale of sound intensity. Every 10 db represents a tenfold increase in intensity. Sounds below 10 db are barely audible; above 140 db they may cause hearing damage. The gray silhouette shows the outer, middle, and inner ear. Sound sets the eardrum vibrating, and this motion is passed on by three small bones (the malleus, incus, and stapes) to the inner ear, where sensitive, hairlike fibers in the cochlea transmit it to the acoustic nerve.

Places such as restaurants, offices, schools, and libraries serve very different functions and therefore require different acoustical conditions.

Background noise contributes to privacy and peacefulness by covering other, more distracting noises. The noise of a crowded restaurant makes private conversation possible. The low, unobtrusive buzz of an electrical system in an open office space masks sounds that could distract workers' attention.

Physiological and Psychological

Although an intangible and invisible energy form, sound has proven capable of exerting a very real influence on our mental and physical health. While pleasing sounds can soothe and delight, prolonged

Since light and sound travel at different speeds, it is possible to calculate the distance at which lightning strikes by measuring the time that passes between the flash and the thunder.

exposure to excessive sound can cause a range of adverse effects from headaches and irritability to such serious maladies as hearing damage, ulcers, hypertension, and heart attacks in people with heart trouble. For these and other reasons, a lot of sound has become recognized as noise pollution. Regulations designed to keep noise at acceptable levels have forced changes in the designs of many machines. Rules governing the permissible locations and times of many activities have been made to protect the hours of sleep and relaxation of communities. These and other laws serve an invaluable purpose, because although it is good to be able to hear that tree falling in the forest, no one wants to listen to it all the time.

Adhesives

Without adhesives, the world wouldn't necessarily come unstuck, but it would be quite a different place from the one we know.

Adhesives, substances that make one thing stick to another like or unlike thing, are used in bonding metals, wood, glass, paper, concrete, ceramics, leather, rubber, and plastics. They are especially important in aircraft manufacture and in the building trades, where the complete dependability of the joining is essential.

Egyptian carvings from 1300 B.C. show workmen gluing a thin piece of veneer to a wooden plank. The Egyptians' papyrus, which served as a writing material in the same way we use paper today, was made by bonding strips of a reedlike plant together with flour-and-water paste (the best papyrus, incidentally, came from Byblos in Lebanon, whence the word "bible"). Coal tar, pine pitch, and beeswax were early natural adhesives that were used for centuries as protective coatings and sealing agents, as well as for sticking things together. Medieval artists in monasteries and convents who illuminated manuscripts used egg white as an adhesive for gold leaf, as did Renaissance painters. Carpenters from the earliest days used glues made from fish, horn, cheese, and other natural materials, and in many nonindustrialized countries boiling, smelly fish glue is used to bond pieces of wood together.

Modern Adhesives

Although new adhesives made from rubber and cellulose were developed during the 19th century, the greatest advances in the field have been made in the present century, especially with the development of the aircraft industry, where good bonding is truly a matter of life and death. Aircraft manufacturers needed bonding agents that assured a high standard of structural strength together with resistance to fatigue (in the sense of "metal fatigue," that is, the weakening of structural metals under continued stress) and the ability to withstand extreme environmental stresses. To meet these demands, chemists developed new products such as epoxy resins, which are based on a process called polymerization. Polymerization is a chemical reaction in which two or more molecules combine to form larger molecules that in some cases are supermolecules, with a basic molecular unit repeated over and over again.

When the demand for adhesives increased greatly in the 1960s, much research was carried out to gain a better understanding of exactly what happens in the adhesive process. Chemists advanced the theory that adhesives stick because of close intermolecular contact. Such contact is what holds the solid matter of the Earth together, and proponents of the theory argue that any material is potentially adhesive to a certain extent, even water, and that what are popularly considered true adhesives are simply materials that have this adhesive quality to an extraordinary degree. To achieve ideal conditions for adhesion, both parts of a joint must be as clean as possible (after all, a workman tries to bond wood to wood, for example, not wood to dirt or oil or some other substance on another piece of wood). One requirement for any adhesive is that it must be liquid during some part of the process, since it must flow over a surface and penetrate into all its crevices. The best bonds, moreover, are obtained when whatever stress is later put on the joined surfaces is exerted parallel to the surfaces—that is, when the stress pushes one surface over the other rather than pulling the two apart.

Natural Glues

Everybody has heard of old horses ending up in the glue factory. In fact, the most familiar natural adhesive is animal glue, made from a protein, collagen, found in animal skin, bone, and sinew. When collagen, normally insoluble, is treated with acids, alkalies, or hot water, it is converted gradually to a soluble form. When absolutely pure and processed very carefully, collagen yields gelatin, which is valuable both as a food and for making photographic color filters. When treated in bulk and with less need for chemical purity, it yields the darker, sludgy product known as animal glue. For centuries, animal glue was used in cabinetmaking, bookbinding, and the preparation of heavy-duty gummed tapes. The animal glue used today is usually modified by chemical additives to improve its qualities.

Another natural adhesive is *casein* glue, made by treating casein, a milk protein, in an alkaline solvent (for the definition of an alkaline solvent, *see* ACIDS AND BASES). Casein glues are more satisfactory for bonding woods than animal glue is, and they are also used in paints and varnishes for their high quality of adhesion. Another natural glue made from fresh or dehydrated slaughterhouse blood is still used in the lumber industry, where thin sheets of wood are bonded together under pressure to make the familiar product known as plywood. The commonest vegetable adhesive is simple flour-and-water paste, which served as the adhesive for wallpaper in the homes of almost everybody's grandparents (and which, with eggs and salt added, is the raw material for making pasta, such as spaghetti and macaroni, the Italian word being the one from which we get not only "paste" but "pastry").

Most adhesives today are synthetic resins, man-made and based on the complex substances called polymers. They fall into two broad classes—*thermoplastic* and *thermosetting*.

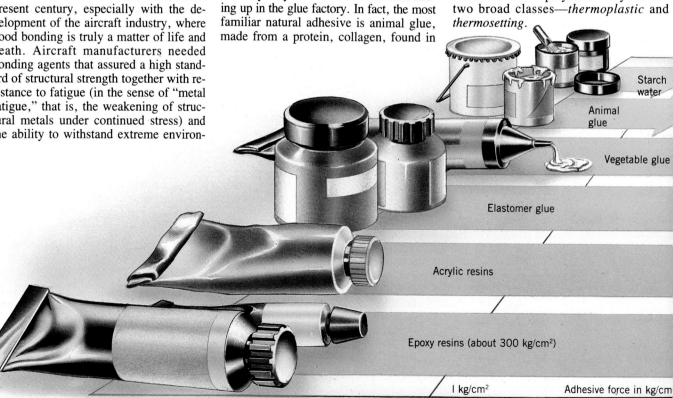

Starch
water

Animal
glue

Vegetable glue

Elastomer glue

Acrylic resins

Epoxy resins (about 300 kg/cm²)

I kg/cm²   Adhesive force in kg/cm

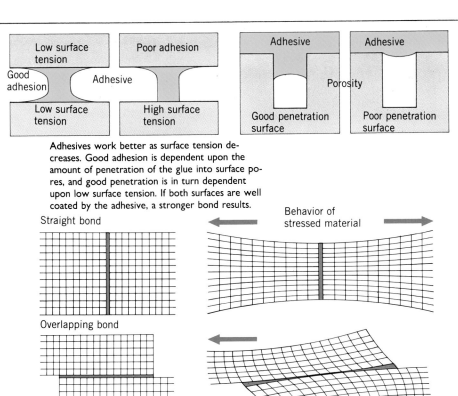

Adhesives work better as surface tension decreases. Good adhesion is dependent upon the amount of penetration of the glue into surface pores, and good penetration is in turn dependent upon low surface tension. If both surfaces are well coated by the adhesive, a stronger bond results.

Straight bond

Behavior of stressed material

Overlapping bond

Diagonal bond

Thermoplastic Adhesives

"Thermoplastic" is simply a technical adjective describing a substance that softens when heated and hardens again as it cools. The thermoplastic resins that serve as adhesives are chiefly either vinyl resins or cellulose derivatives. The former all contain an organic group of atoms called vinyl in their molecules. The adhesives set either by heating followed by cooling or by evaporation of the liquid part of the solvent. One vinyl adhesive is vinyl acetate, made by the reaction of the familiar gas acetylene (used in welding torches) with acetic acid, which is the principal component of vinegar. When polymer-ized, vinyl acetate becomes the white emulsion now used almost universally as a household glue. Other vinyl resins are used in bonding sheets of glass together to make shatterproof windshields and windows.

Cellulose derivatives are made from cellulose acetate and cellulose nitrate, two compounds made by treating cellulose (the principal component of plant cell walls) with acids and dissolving the resulting product in quick-drying solvents. These adhesives are satisfactory for bonding wood and paper but do not work well with metals and glass.

Thermosetting Adhesives

Thermosetting adhesives (as opposed to thermoplastic) are made with synthetic resins, which, when they harden, undergo an irreversible chemical change that renders them unmeltable and insoluble over the range of temperatures normally encountered. They find wide applications in industry, from cementing plastic sheets like Formica onto wood bases to creating water-resistant, weather-resistant bonds in building and boat construction. Epoxies make use of special organic compounds (called epoxides because they include extra oxygen atoms in their molecules) that are mixed with a catalyst, which is a substance used to encourage a chemical reaction without actually taking part in it (*see* CATALYST AND CATALYSIS). The bond is later "cured," that is, hardened, by heating, although some harden at room temperature. Because epoxies are excellent electric insulators (nonconductors), they find wide uses in the manufacture of electric and electronic apparatus, in aircraft, dentistry, orthopedic surgery, and brain surgery. Surgical adhesives constitute a special class, which can be defined approximately as adhesives that bond tissues without sutures or clamps. At least one among these is popularly known as "crazy glue," the kind that you have to be very careful in using so that if, in the middle of the job, you brush your hair back, you don't end up with your hand temporarily but firmly fixed to your forehead or scalp!

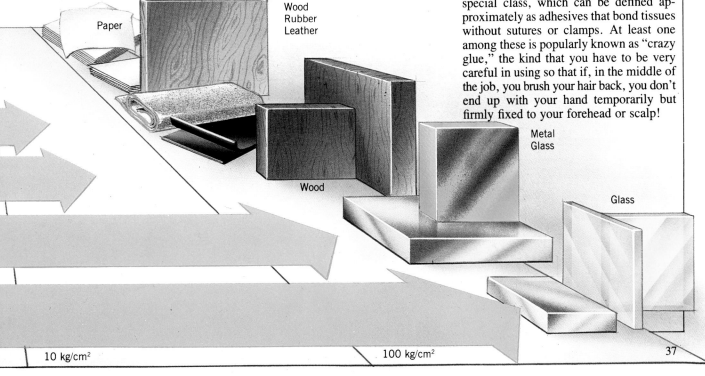

Paper

Wood
Rubber
Leather

Wood

Metal
Glass

Glass

10 kg/cm²

100 kg/cm²

Adrenal Gland

In the 1850s, British physician Thomas Addison treated a patient who had baffling symptoms: increasing anemia, feebleness of the heart, and a tanned pigmentation of the skin that did not respond to any treatment. The patient died. Over a 5-year period, Dr. Addison performed autopsies in similar cases and discovered that the only internal organs affected were the little adrenal glands, which lie on top of the kidneys. These were withered and shrunken into tiny fibrous beads.

Until then, no one had known what functions these glands served. But here was evidence that the adrenals were essential to life, that they somehow helped maintain the normal functioning of the heart, digestive organs, blood, and skin, and played a vital role in the growth and maintenance of fatty and muscular tissue. While the doctor did not discover the cure for the mysterious disease, it was named Addison's disease; thousands of researchers since then have studied the adrenal glands and the hormones they produce.

Hormones

The adrenal glands are two separate glands that produce more than 50 hormones. They are part of the endocrine system of ductless glands, which, together with the central nervous system, regulates our bodily functions. Each adrenal gland is divided into an outer bark-

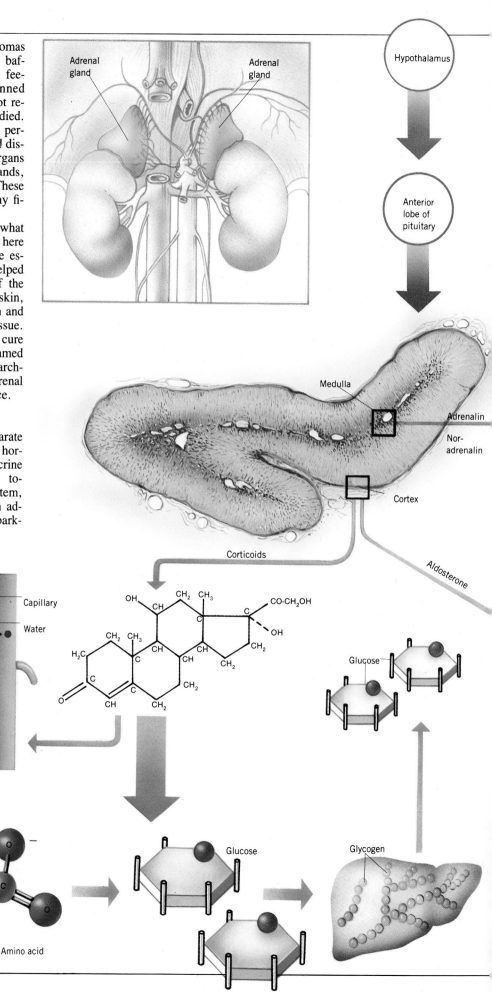

like layer, the adrenal cortex, and the inner medulla.

The medulla secretes adrenalin and noradrenalin, hormones that affect a number of organs including the heart and blood vessels. Noradrenalin also plays an important part in transmission of nerve impulses. Adrenalin and noradrenalin produce the so-called fight-or-flight reactions in response to emergencies. These hormones trigger a rise in blood pressure, increase the rate and force of heartbeat, and make more blood sugar available for energy.

The adrenal cortex in many ways is the more important part of the gland, secreting dozens of hormones known as adrenocortical steroids. An insufficiency in these cortical hormones will disrupt many bodily functions. A rise in the concentration of potassium in the blood and a corresponding decline in the level of sodium will occur. Carbohydrate metabolism and muscle, nerve, and kidney function will also be impaired. The results are weakness, weight loss, and an increase of toxic wastes in the blood—all classic symptoms of Addison's disease. In 1927, researchers discovered that an extract of the adrenal cortices relieved these symptoms in dogs whose glands had been removed. From there, it was only a matter of a few years before adrenal cortical extracts were made available for humans.

Adrenocortical Steroids

The various adrenocortical steroids differ in chemical makeup by only a few atoms, but their actions are very different. Several classes of steroid hormones have been distinguished. The first comprises sex hormones. The adrenal cortex is the only endocrine gland, other than the sex glands (testes and ovaries), that secretes androgens, male sex hormones.

More important are the mineralocorticoids, such as aldosterone. These act on the kidneys to regulate the balance of sodium, potassium, chloride, and water in the blood and body tissues, essential in maintaining the body's homeostasis, or chemical and fluid balance.

The largest and most complex class of cortical hormones comprises the glucocorticoids, such as cortisone, hydrocortisone, and corticosterone. Multiple in their effects, they regulate the metabolism of fats, proteins, and carbohydrates and the formation of glycogen (blood sugar) by the liver.

The glucocorticoids also inhibit the inflammatory response to tissue damage. (For this reason, athletes with injuries often receive injections of cortisone.) They also suppress allergic reactions caused by the release of the hormone histamine and other substances from the tissues. Unfortunately, glucocorticoids also have extremely severe side effects when used in large quantities over a long span of time. They have been shown to cause stomach ulcers, high blood pressure, psychological changes, brittle bones, excessive hair growth, and decreased resistance to certain types of infection. Doctors prescribing them must always evaluate their potential for harm together with their possible benefits to the patient.

The adrenal glands sit above the kidneys and consist of two parts: cortex and medulla. The glands are controlled by a feedback system of the hypothalamus and the pituitary. The adrenal cortex is essential to life. It controls the formation of glycogen (form of stored glucose), along with the elimination of potassium and the retention of sodium in the kidneys. The adrenal medulla prepares the body for emergency action. Hormones from the medulla cause constriction of arteries, dilation of bronchial tubes, rise in blood pressure, and conversion of glycogen to glucose as a response to danger or injury.

Constriction of arteries

Dilation of bronchial tubes

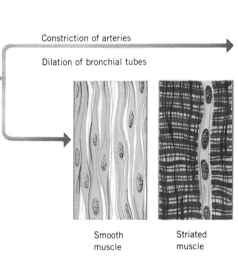

Smooth muscle

Striated muscle

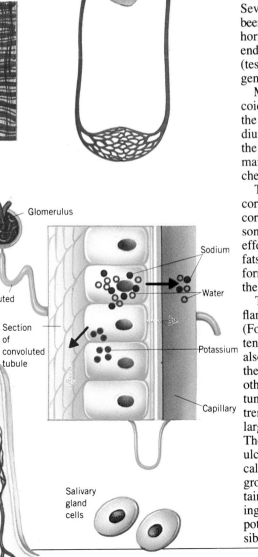

Glomerulus

Convoluted tubule

Section of convoluted tubule

Sodium

Water

Potassium

Capillary

Intestinal villi

Sweat gland

Salivary gland cells

Aerial Photography

Surely the most striking aerial photography ever made is the color photograph of the Earth taken by Apollo 8 astronauts Frank Borman, James Lovell, Jr., and William A. Anders from 100,000 miles (160,000 km) out in space while on their way to lunar orbit in December 1968. That such a photograph of our planet could ever be made seemed quite impossible a generation ago, like some wild dream of a science-fiction writer. The photograph marked the culmination of a long process that started over a century ago, when the first aerial photograph was made by "aeronaut" Félix Nadar from a captive balloon in 1858.

World War I demonstrated the great effectiveness of aerial photography in warfare, and in the period between the wars an entire new science, photogrammetry, was developed. Photogrammetry is the science of making measurements from aerial photographs, and its most important peacetime use is in map-making. The technique has developed to such a degree of perfection that aerial photographers can shoot pictures at an altitude of 100,000 feet (30.45 km) with such wealth of detail that objects measuring a few inches (5-6 cm) in length or breadth can be clearly seen.

In mapping by aerial photography, the basic problem is to achieve as literal and detailed a shot of the terrain as possible. Different sections of the terrain are photographed by special cameras mounted on aircraft that follow parallel flight lines at equal altitudes. This permits mounting the photographs with the west side, for example, of one shot overlapping the eastern edge of the adjacent picture, to give a smooth overall picture that technicians in the field call a mosaic. Almost the entire continent of North America has been photographed in this way, as well as a good part of the rest of the world.

Indispensable to aerial photography is the photo interpreter, whose job it is to derive a wealth of information from the pictures made by aerial cameras mounted on aircraft, rockets, or satellites. A skilled photo interpreter can pinpoint and identify practically every kind of natural and man-made feature covered by the photograph. Areas that once could be mapped only by making long and dangerous expeditions into often inhospitable territory can now be readily mapped by aerial photographers and interpreted accurately by expert photo interpreters.

Until fairly recently, most aerial photography was done with black and white film, but in recent years, color film has proved increasingly useful in studying vegetation, rock formations, and types of soil—indeed, almost all aspects of surface geology. Planners of aerial-photog-

The motion of the airplane and of the camera as it takes photographs in flight makes necessary a series of complicated calculations that take into account the height and velocity at which the aircraft is moving in order to correctly line up each single photograph with the next.

Most of these calculations are now done automatically by microcomputers and by the use of particular reference points that appear in more than one frame, like the mountain top marked V at the right.

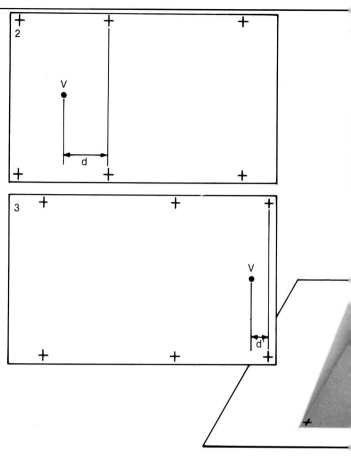

raphy projects also have at their disposal a type of film called false-color film, in which some colors occurring in nature can be exaggerated to bring out features that would otherwise be barely visible. Developed as a military technique for recognizing camouflage in hostile territory, the film has found important applications in agriculture and botany, particularly in the study of plant disease.

The development of Earth-orbiting satellites since the late 1950s has made it possible to take photographs from much higher altitudes than was possible in the days when only conventional aircraft were available. A satellite flying at an altitude of several hundred miles (3,500 km or more) can carry cameras that take pictures of entire continents. Even more sophisticated terrain sensors make use of infrared photography for studying the composition of the soil and ocean currents; of radar for studying soil characteristics, movement of ocean and land ice, and tsunami (tidal wave) warnings; and of spectroscopic techniques for locating mineral deposits and oil. All of these have greatly expanded the original scope of observation from simple aerial photography to full exploitation of new and complex instrumentation.

The importance of the new techniques can be shown by a striking example. With infrared cameras that use the part of the electromagnetic spectrum lying just beyond the red end of the visible spectrum (*see* ELECTROMAGNETISM AND SPECTRUM), photographs of terrain can be made in presunrise hours that reveal details not visible in photographs taken during the day. Photo interpreters have learned how to spot potential landslides in such infrared photographs, giving geologists early warnings of such problem situations.

Aerial photographs provide an instantaneous historical record of any given part of the Earth. By comparing photographs of the same terrain taken months or years apart, geologists can easily chart changes that have taken place. Photographs are also useful in studying terrain for mineral or petroleum deposits, thus reducing immeasurably the labor and expense involved in prospecting. In undeveloped regions, photographs taken from the sky can given soil scientists leads to potential agricultural areas. In forestry, aerial photography is an invaluable tool in estimating the amount of timber available and in determining damage after floods or fires. Government sleuths have also used aerial photography to spot illegal marijuana crops from the air.

Modern military forces could scarcely exist without aerial photography, a technique largely developed by them. Today,

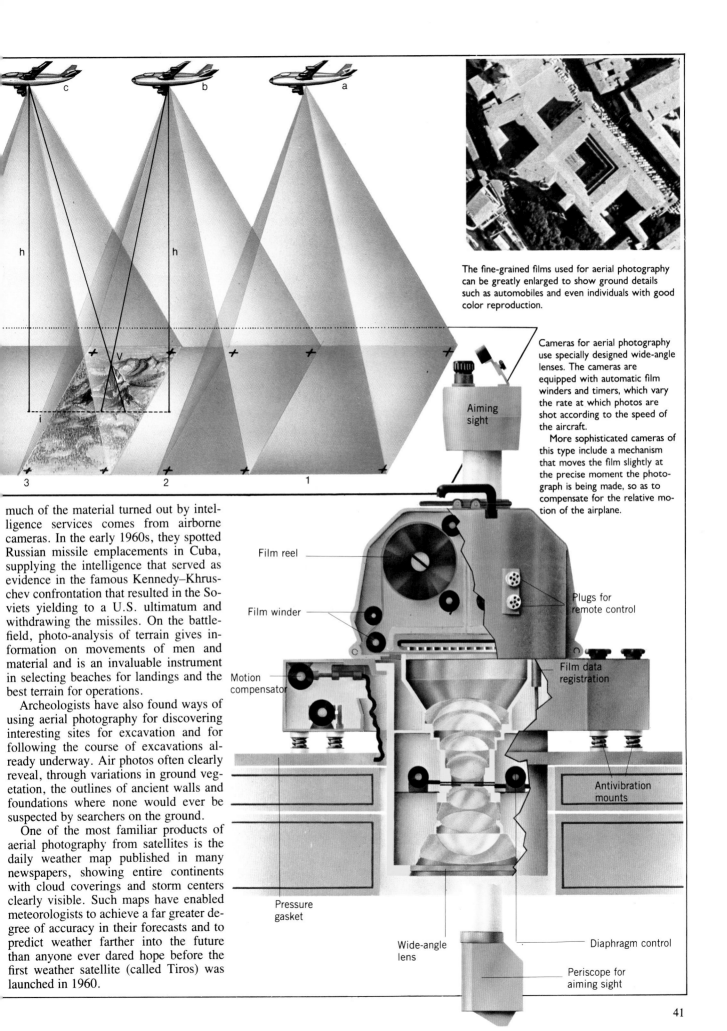

The fine-grained films used for aerial photography can be greatly enlarged to show ground details such as automobiles and even individuals with good color reproduction.

Cameras for aerial photography use specially designed wide-angle lenses. The cameras are equipped with automatic film winders and timers, which vary the rate at which photos are shot according to the speed of the aircraft.

More sophisticated cameras of this type include a mechanism that moves the film slightly at the precise moment the photograph is being made, so as to compensate for the relative motion of the airplane.

Aiming sight

Film reel

Film winder

Plugs for remote control

Motion compensator

Film data registration

Antivibration mounts

Pressure gasket

Wide-angle lens

Diaphragm control

Periscope for aiming sight

much of the material turned out by intelligence services comes from airborne cameras. In the early 1960s, they spotted Russian missile emplacements in Cuba, supplying the intelligence that served as evidence in the famous Kennedy–Khruschev confrontation that resulted in the Soviets yielding to a U.S. ultimatum and withdrawing the missiles. On the battlefield, photo-analysis of terrain gives information on movements of men and material and is an invaluable instrument in selecting beaches for landings and the best terrain for operations.

Archeologists have also found ways of using aerial photography for discovering interesting sites for excavation and for following the course of excavations already underway. Air photos often clearly reveal, through variations in ground vegetation, the outlines of ancient walls and foundations where none would ever be suspected by searchers on the ground.

One of the most familiar products of aerial photography from satellites is the daily weather map published in many newspapers, showing entire continents with cloud coverings and storm centers clearly visible. Such maps have enabled meteorologists to achieve a far greater degree of accuracy in their forecasts and to predict weather farther into the future than anyone ever dared hope before the first weather satellite (called Tiros) was launched in 1960.

Aerodynamics and Aeronautics

High on the brink of a cliff stands a man. Around him is a brightly colored, metal-and-cloth contraption that looks like a kite. As the huge rollers of the Pacific Ocean surge 500 feet (150 m) below, the man takes a step forward. The cloth about his shoulders blossoms into a V-shaped wing, and in an instant the man is soaring freely above the vertiginous depths.

The most important application of aerodynamics—the study of how objects interact with air—has been man's conquest of the air; in less than a century, it has made flying our swiftest and most efficient mode of long-distance transport.

The Working of an Airplane

Think of yourself standing in an open field in a strong wind. The wind presses against your body, making it difficult to maintain an upright posture. If you hold your hand out flat, you will also feel the pressure; if you angle it into the wind, you will feel the pressure turning it to one side or the other. You are using your hand as an airfoil, a shape that interacts with air.

Is this what makes an airplane fly? No, although it is what makes a kite fly.

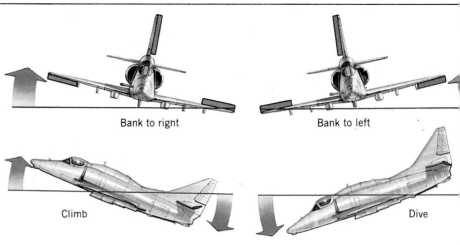

Bank to right   Bank to left

Climb   Dive

Moving the wing and the tail surfaces through the use of rudders and flaps controls the direction of flight.

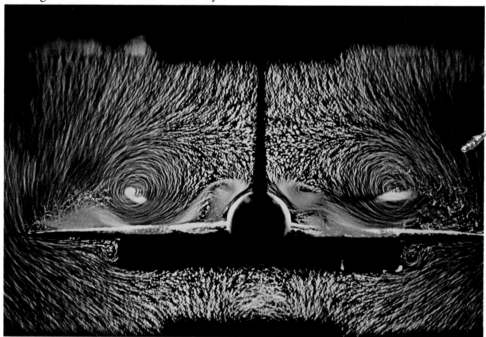

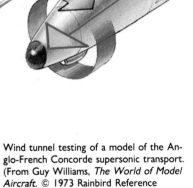

Wind tunnel testing of a model of the Anglo-French Concorde supersonic transport. (From Guy Williams, *The World of Model Aircraft*. © 1973 Rainbird Reference Books)

Whereas a kite is pushed into the air by wind pressure, an airplane is lifted into the air by a force appropriately called lift.

Lift is created by moving air, like the wind pressing against your hand as you stand in the windy field. Suppose we carry this picture a bit farther.

As you hold your hand out flat into the wind while rotating it at the wrist, tilting it up or down, you will feel wind pressure working against it. Now, by cupping your fingers slightly, give your hand a curved shape. The force of the wind will seem to lessen as the air flows smoothly up and over the curved surface of your hand. Actually, it is not lessening, it is just that the air is flowing more smoothly over the curved surface.

By curving your hand, you have given it an aerodynamic shape. Almost 250 years ago, a Swiss mathematician, Daniel Bernoulli, demonstrated how this affects the flow of air, and in so doing he discovered the basic scientific secret that makes flight possible.

Air flows in streams and currents, the way water does. By smoothing out and curving surfaces, Bernoulli found that water could be made to flow smoothly over and around an object without creating disturbing eddies and bubbles. A fish is a beautiful illustration of this. The head is rounded, with no sharp edges, and it blends smoothly into the body, which flows smoothly into the tail. This is called streamlining, and Bernoulli reasoned correctly that it applies just as much to air as to water.

But that is only the beginning of the story; Bernoulli also found that streamlining a surface makes the air flow faster over it. The air current at once speeding up and

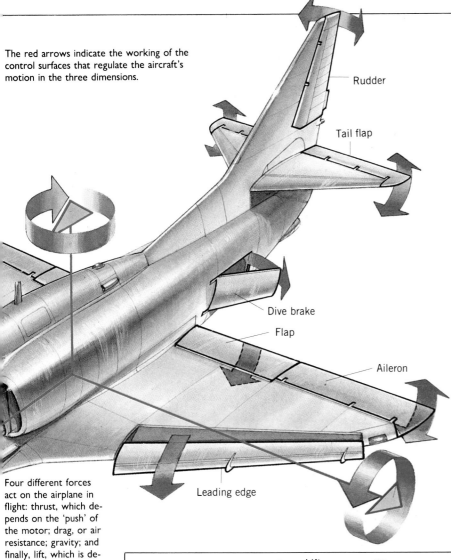

Rudder

Tail flap

Dive brake

Flap

Aileron

Leading edge

Four different forces act on the airplane in flight: thrust, which depends on the 'push' of the motor; drag, or air resistance; gravity; and finally, lift, which is determined by the shape of the wing.

A wing lifts the aircraft in moving air because it has a greater curve on the upper side than on the bottom. The result is that the air flowing over the wing has to travel farther than the air below, thus must move more rapidly. This causes a pressure differential that, in effect, 'sucks' the wing upward.

Lift is even more marked when the wing is set at a slight angle. The bowl of a spoon in a stream of water demonstrates the effect. The curved back is pulled toward the water flow. The greater the angle, the stronger the force acting on the spoon.

The two airfoils below show that the same thing happens in a stream of air.

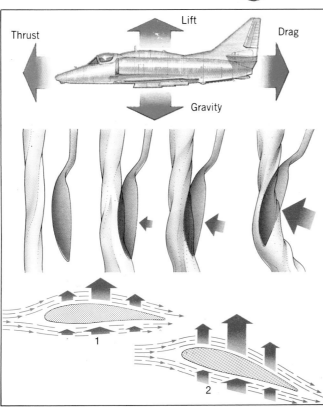

Thrust

Lift

Drag

Gravity

1

2

thinning out no longer follows the surface beyond a certain point but breaks from it, moving gradually away. This leaves a space between the bottom layer of the air current and the upper surface of the object—and in this space, Bernoulli found there are turbulent variations of pressure. The thinned-out, and therefore lower-pressure, fast-flowing air above is exerting a "pulling" effort on this turbulent space and the streamlined surface beneath. In other words, it is trying to lift it upward.

The Amazing Power of Lift

The strength of this lifting force can be measured by placing tubes of mercury at intervals along the upper surface of an airplane wing. Depending on the type of wing and the speed of the airflow, it may be able to create enough lift to pick up 30, 40, 50 or more pounds per square foot (1.3, 1.7, 2.1 kg per sq m) of wing surface.

The first man to demonstrate the principle of lift with a full-sized airplane was Otto Lilienthal, a German aviation pioneer. In the 1880s, he built a series of gliders that he flew off a hill he himself had built near Berlin. Keeping careful notes on each flight, he amassed the first body of aerodynamic performance statistics. He did experiments with various kinds of wing curvature, or camber, which proved extremely helpful to others who followed his pursuits of the secret of flight.

Lilienthal was killed in 1896, but hard on his heels came the Wright brothers, Orville and Wilbur. Using Lilienthal's figures, they found his system of controlling flight by shifting body weight to be unsatisfactory. They came up with a system of their own, based on bird flight. They observed that birds turned, and banked in turns, by twisting or warping the feathers at their wingtips. The Wrights devised their own way of warping the wingtips, and with this perfected, they achieved the first powered flight of an airplane on December 17, 1903, at Kitty Hawk, North Carolina. Their wing-warping system was subsequently refined into the aileron system (system of movable flaps on the wings) that we know today.

The first Wright Flyer, as it was known, was far from being an aerodynamic ideal. As anyone can see who observes the original, hanging in the National Air and Space Museum in Washington, D.C., it is a boxy and ungainly contraption of wood and bracing wires, with large, square wings and two huge wooden propellers turned—or "swung," as aviators say—by a home-built gasoline engine. The Wrights were mainly concerned with achieving the minimum necessary lift; the niceties of efficient aerodynamics were

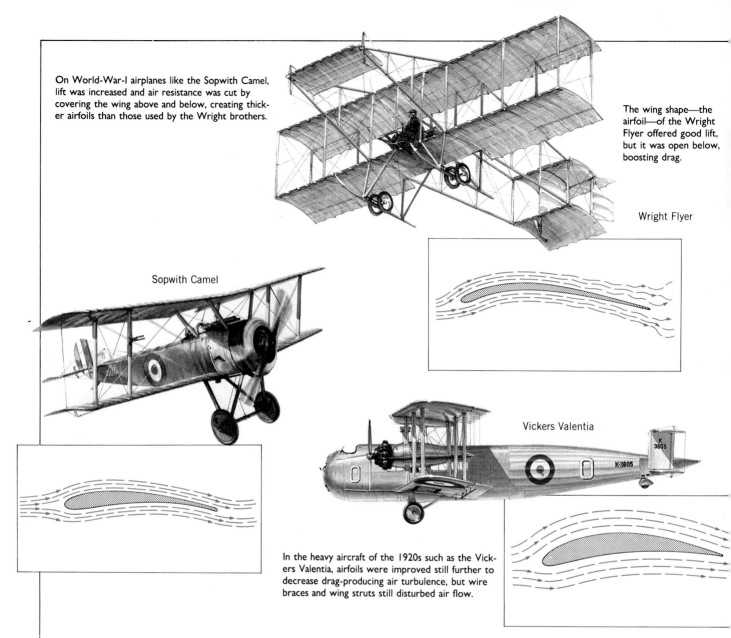

On World-War-I airplanes like the Sopwith Camel, lift was increased and air resistance was cut by covering the wing above and below, creating thicker airfoils than those used by the Wright brothers.

The wing shape—the airfoil—of the Wright Flyer offered good lift, but it was open below, boosting drag.

Wright Flyer

Sopwith Camel

Vickers Valentia

In the heavy aircraft of the 1920s such as the Vickers Valentia, airfoils were improved still further to decrease drag-producing air turbulence, but wire braces and wing struts still disturbed air flow.

still in the future. The wing was the main thing, and for the next decade or so it remained the chief center of attraction in the developing aviation industry.

The Airfoil and the Development of Modern Aircraft

Wings are the primary airfoils that interact with the air to make an airplane fly. Since an infinity of curves can be designed for airfoils, it was necessary for early airplane designers to categorize the basic types that would be useful in flight. Within a short time, such basic types began to emerge. Thick wings with steep curves at the front, or leading edge, were the best lifters, but because of their bluntness they were slow fliers. Moving the high point of curvature, or camber, back along the wing improved the pilot's con-

trol in flight. Thin wings were best for speed, but they were tricky to handle, requiring great skill. In general, it was some variation on the thick wing, with its high lifting capacity, that dominated aviation up to the 1930s.

Streamlining, after airfoil design perhaps the most important aspect of aerodynamics, was largely unknown and unpracticed in those days, except in racing machines. Most airplanes presented all sorts of square and flat surfaces to the wind, and were everywhere encumbered by struts and wires, which were used either to brace parts of the airplane or to work the controls. Even when airplane bodies were built that could accommodate a pilot, passengers, mail, or freight, they were still more like boxes fastened to the wings than a smoothly integrated unit. As late as

1931, Germany built an airliner, the Junkers G-38, with a wing so thick that passengers could be seated inside it. It was the biggest airplane in the world.

The slow, square aircraft did much to impede the expansion of aviation into its destined realm of fast, efficient passenger transport. But in 1933, an entirely different "breakthrough" airplane was designed for United Airlines—the Boeing 247. A twin-engined plane with a single, low wing and landing gear that pulled up and folded away out of sight when it was flying, the 247 presented no flat or angular surfaces whatever to the wind of its passing. It was built entirely of metal, with all bracing and control wires concealed inside. Compared to most of the airplanes in those days, it looked as revolutionary as a rocket, and it could fly from New

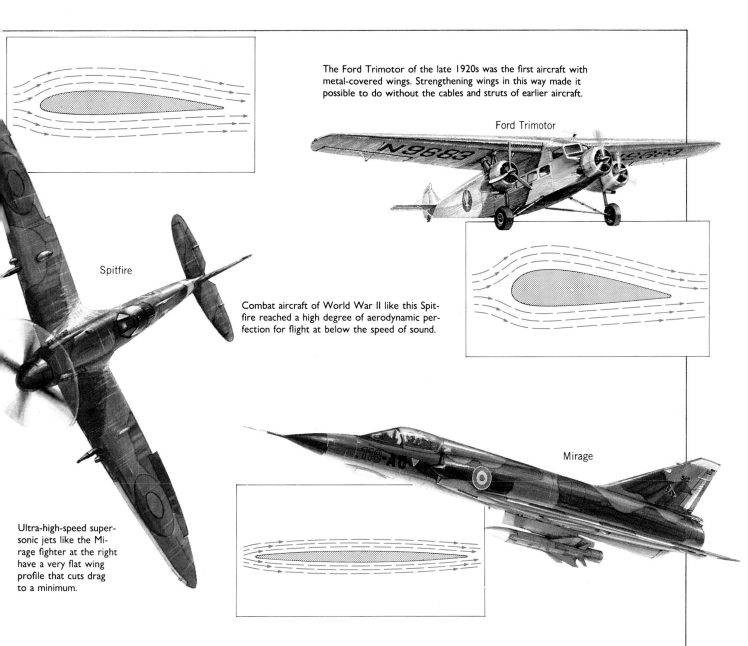

The Ford Trimotor of the late 1920s was the first aircraft with metal-covered wings. Strengthening wings in this way made it possible to do without the cables and struts of earlier aircraft.

Ford Trimotor

Spitfire

Combat aircraft of World War II like this Spitfire reached a high degree of aerodynamic perfection for flight at below the speed of sound.

Mirage

Ultra-high-speed supersonic jets like the Mirage fighter at the right have a very flat wing profile that cuts drag to a minimum.

York to California with 10 passengers in a little less than 20 hours.

The 247 was an aerodynamic pioneer. It did not carry quite the load expected, however, and it was soon superseded by another, strikingly similar airplane, the Douglas DC-1. Designed by Donald Wills Douglas, a newcomer to the field, the DC-1 could carry four more passengers than the 247 at the same operating costs. The DC-1 soon gave way to the DC-2, and then came a real eye-opener, the Douglas Sleeper Transport, or DST. Here, for the first time, was total comfort in an airplane—not only were hot meals served by stewardesses, but there were bunks so that passengers could sleep away the tedious hours on long-distance flights. In its daytime version the DST, which was basi-

cally a DC-2 with a widened fuselage, could carry 21 people.

The DC-3, as the DST soon became known, was probably the most famous airplane ever built, and certainly the longest-lived. More DC-3s were built than any other airplane, and in World War II they served on all fronts all over the world. In the United States alone, 11,000 were built, and the Soviet Union manufactured another 2,000 under license. Today, almost half a century after it made its debut, the DC-3 is still in service all over the world.

The advent of the jet engine after World War II brought further revolutionary changes in practical aerodynamics. The enormous power of the jets could virtually fling airplanes into the air, and the preeminence of high-lift, thick wings gave

way now to much thinner airfoils that could take full advantage of the jets' speed potential. Streamlining became of paramount importance, for the new generation of transports could travel at twice the speed of the old, prop-driven types, and their altitude capabilities reached into the stratosphere.

It might be said that the laws of aerodynamics were "stretched" to accommodate the new aircraft, so everything about them was bigger, higher, faster. This made passenger loads of 350 to 450 people possible, as well as huge quantities of freight. In less than a century since Otto Lilienthal and the Wright brothers made their pioneering experiments with the lift-producing airfoil, that airfoil has transformed the world.

Aerosol Sprays

Although the word "aerosol" commonly brings to mind the aerosol spray device, it technically refers to tiny liquid or solid particles dispersed in a gas. An aerosol is also called a colloid. One example of a natural aerosol is a cloud, which is made up of small drops of water held together and contained by air. The volcanic cloud produced by the Mount St. Helens eruption was the largest natural aerosol in recent history.

A man-made aerosol is also a colloid, composed of active ingredients and propellant gases. The active ingredients are chemicals used to perform certain tasks. They may be deodorants, pesticides, cleansers, or other substances. The active ingredients are dispersed in the propellants—the gases that carry the aerosol out of the container.

How an Aerosol Spray Works

An aerosol spray works very much like a champagne bottle popping its cork. With the cork lodged securely in the neck of the bottle, the gas in champagne is trapped inside. When the cork is slightly loosened, however, the strength of the trapped gas pressing outward is sufficient to dislodge the cork and shoot it out of the bottle. In an aerosol device, the propellant gases are trapped inside until the valve is opened. Then the propellant rushes toward the opening, either pushing or carrying the active ingredients along with it.

Inside the neck of the aerosol spray is a rubber collar that seals the valve. Downward pressure on the aerosol cap moves the valve below the gasket, opening it so that solution can rise from the bottom of the container through a long, thin, hollow tube.

There are two kinds of pressure systems used in aerosol sprays. In one, the propellant is packed separately at the top and exerts a downward pressure on the solution; this drives the active ingredients up the tube and out of the container. Propellants used in this system expand to occupy the space left by the active ingredients leaving the container.

In the other kind of pressure system, the propellant and active ingredients are mixed together. When the valve opens, the propellant rushes out, carrying the ingredients dispersed in it. As the solution of active ingredients and propellant is dispensed, propellant molecules vaporize and fill the space at the top of the container, creating a layer of vapor pressure. In between the vapor layer and the solution, a mixture of vapor and solution forms. When an aerosol container is almost empty, bubbles come out of the nozzle, indicating that only the vapor-and-solution mixture is left.

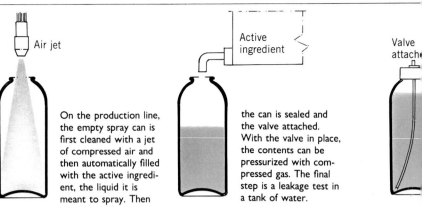

On the production line, the empty spray can is first cleaned with a jet of compressed air and then automatically filled with the active ingredient, the liquid it is meant to spray. Then the can is sealed and the valve attached. With the valve in place, the contents can be pressurized with compressed gas. The final step is a leakage test in a tank of water.

Propellants

Propellants include such gases as butane, chlorinated hydrocarbons, isobutane, propane, vinyl chloride, and nitrogen. A group of propellants called fluorocarbons (Freon is one well-known fluorocarbon trade name) were among the most popular propellants until the late 1970s, when they came under attack as extremely dangerous pollutants. Fluorocarbons, which consist of fluorine, chlorine, and carbon, break down in the presence of sunlight and release chlorine monoxide molecules. These molecules then persist in the atmosphere, resisting further breakdown or combination with other molecules. Chlorine monoxide molecules are considered potentially hazardous because they break down molecules of the ozone, a layer of atmosphere that shields the Earth from dangerous ultraviolet radiation from the Sun. In 1978, the fluorocarbon group was singled out as an environmental menace and banned from the U.S. market.

Aerosols with other propellants are selling well despite the fluorocarbon scare, however, and are performing more household, workshop, agricultural, and industrial tasks than ever before. In the United States, fluorocarbons have been replaced by other Food and Drug Administration-approved propellants, and variations on the aerosol system continue to be developed. One of the most environmentally sound aerosol systems recently invented harnesses the pressure power produced by a carbon dioxide reaction. The propellant ingredients are stored in a plastic sac inside an aerosol container. The sac contains a small amount of carbon dioxide, which acts as a pressurizer. At the bottom of the sac is a pool of citric acid; at the top are sealed pockets containing sodium bicarbonate tablets. The aerosol product occupies the container space outside the sac. As the product is dispensed from the container, the carbon dioxide-filled sac expands and breaks the seal of the lowest pocket. A sodium bicarbonate tablet drops out of the pocket and falls into the pool of citric acid, forming more carbon dioxide. As the container empties of active ingredients, the carbon dioxide in the plastic sac continues to expand and create new gas to take up more and more of the space in the container. This ingenious device provides the convenience of aerosol sprays without harming the environment.

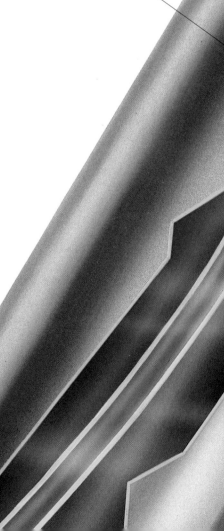

Compressed gas

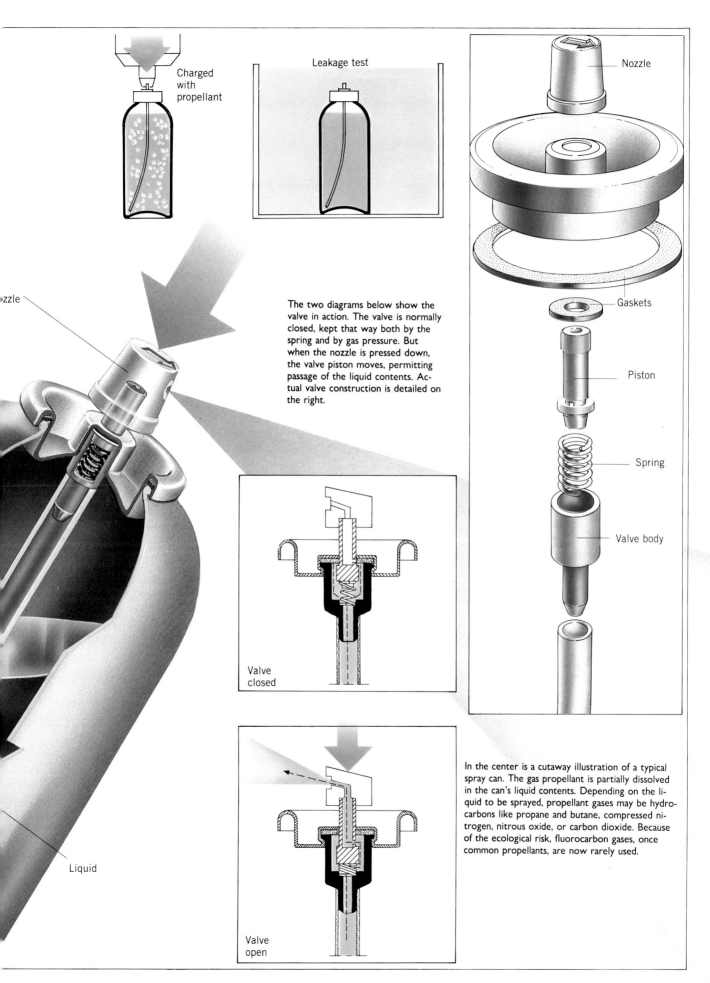

Charged
with
propellant

Leakage test

Nozzle

Gaskets

Piston

Spring

Valve body

zzle

The two diagrams below show the valve in action. The valve is normally closed, kept that way both by the spring and by gas pressure. But when the nozzle is pressed down, the valve piston moves, permitting passage of the liquid contents. Actual valve construction is detailed on the right.

Liquid

Valve
closed

Valve
open

In the center is a cutaway illustration of a typical spray can. The gas propellant is partially dissolved in the can's liquid contents. Depending on the liquid to be sprayed, propellant gases may be hydrocarbons like propane and butane, compressed nitrogen, nitrous oxide, or carbon dioxide. Because of the ecological risk, fluorocarbon gases, once common propellants, are now rarely used.

Aging

No one wants to get old, but most everyone prefers it to the alternative, death. Aging is a natural part of the life cycle. Scientists divide aging into two types. Primary aging, or senescence, refers to the unavoidable, irreversible, and cumulative changes in body structure and composition during that part of the lifespan after maturity is reached. Secondary aging, or senility, which includes disabilities caused by illness or accidental damage, is not inevitably a part of old age.

Organ and Systemic Changes

Aging is the process of change that leads to increased risk of debility, disease, and finally death. Very few people actually die of old age itself; most die of diseases to which the aging process makes them more vulnerable. This process includes several basic kinds of degeneration. Usually, the heart pumps less blood per minute. Mus-

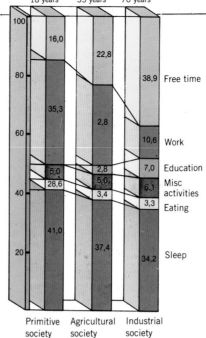

	18 years	35 years	70 years	
	16,0	22,8	38,9	Free time
	35,3	2,8	10,6	Work
	5,0	2,8	7,0	Education
	28,6	5,0	6,1	Misc activities
		3,4	3,3	Eating
	41,0	37,4	34,2	Sleep
Primitive society	Agricultural society	Industrial society		

Left: The bar graph shows how the amount of time dedicated to different activities has changed in the progression from a primitive culture to a modern industrial society.
Below: the two diagrams illustrate the differences between the transmission of nerve impulses in a young subject (left) and an elderly one (right). Impulses are carried within the nerve cell as electrical signals. To jump from one cell to the next, the impulse must be carried by a chemical neurotransmitter like dopamine, as shown here. When the neurotransmitter reaches the next cell, its passage through the cell membrane is governed by the enzymes present. Once inside, neural receptors transform the chemical signal back into an electrical impulse.

In the elderly, this whole process is slowed by a variety of factors: low levels of neurotransmitters, fewer neural receptors, reduced enzyme activity, and relatively impermeable cell membranes.

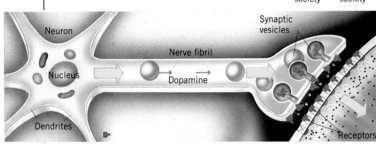

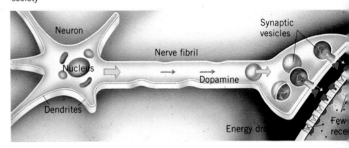

cle strength declines, partly because of lowered blood supply and partly because of a loss of functioning muscle cells. Both male and female sex hormone production falls; for females, it falls sharply after menopause; for males, more gradually, after the age of 50.

The general responsiveness and sensitivity of almost all body functions grow lower with age. Organs that are affected include the brain cells, impairing thought processes; the senses, reducing acuity of perception; and the endocrine system, slowing all chemical reactions directed by enzymes. In fact, the responsiveness of all the body's various adjustments to stress and environmental change is affected to some degree. Many of the functional declines of physical processes in old age, such as reduction in blood-sugar levels, are not caused by a failure of the organs involved (in this case the pancreas) but rather by loss of sensitivity (that is, the pancreas's ability to measure blood sugar levels).

Cellular Changes

Organs and systems fail because of a loss of functioning cells, which reduces reserve capacity, and because of lowered performance of the remaining cells. Lowered responsiveness on the cellular level

means cellular enzymes may be less active, thus requiring more time for chemical reactions. Such retardation may impair or kill cells.

The body has two types or organs: those capable of regenerating their own cells, such as the skin, bone marrow, liver, and lining of the gastrointestinal tract, and those that cannot replace cells, such as the heart, skeletal muscles, brain, and spinal nerves. In either case, aging can cause worn-out cells to be replaced by scar tissue, which can cause organs to fail to function properly if too many cells are lost. Many body organs like the skin contain collagen and elastin, which provide support and elasticity. The fibers of these tissues develop bonds throughout life, leading to a general stiffening. Collagen cross-linking stiffens old skin, so that it stands away from underlying structures, causing sagging and wrinkles.

Structural support for the body is provided by tendons, the ligaments and muscles anchored to strong sturdy bones. Bone strength is in a large part due to an organic matrix that is mineralized with a complex mixture of calcium and phosphorus. This composition is a dynamic system involving constant deposition and reabsorption of minerals. Aging causes reabsorption to occur faster than deposi-

tion, leading to a softening of bone called osteoporosis.

With increasing age, cells are destroyed faster than they are produced, weakening the structural material of the body. Also, fatty material increases in and around cells. Cholesterol plaque builds up on the inside surface of blood vessels, leading to arteriosclerosis, or "hardening of the arteries." This condition can lead to high blood pressure and a decreased blood flow in the damaged vessels. Major organ damage such as heart attack can result from blocked arteries.

Causes of Aging

There are several theories about the causes of the aging process. One theory assumes that life-span is programmed into each person's genes. The error theory suggests that DNA molecules, which carry the information required to build every element of the body, misdirect the building of enzymes. Enzymes control all chemical reactions in the body; a misbuilt enzyme molecule would not work properly, impeding chemical reactions and the processes they direct. The somatic mutation theory proposes that DNA sometimes makes mistakes, causing mutations (or misbuilt cells) throughout life, and aging is due to the accumulation of such abnormal cells. Other theories suggest that impeded cell function is caused by a gradual buildup of waste products (such as age pigments), cross-linking within biologically important molecules, or simple wearing out of cells. The autoimmune theory assumes that the immune system, which attacks invading cells, loses its ability to distinguish between itself and intruders and begins to attack the body's own cells.

Variations in Aging

Theories attempt to dissect the mechanism of aging, but the actual aging process is the result of changes in the complex interrelations of all body systems. Furthermore, different organs age at different rates and respond to aging in different ways. Also, individuals age differently. For example, one person's cardiovascular system at age 50 may be comparable to another's at age 20. Heredity, environmental stress, and general health based on nutrition, exercise, and other factors are all important to the aging process.

Mental decline (the most familiar aspect of senility) is not an inevitable part of aging. In the absence of disease, the elderly can maintain mental acuity, although learning may occur more slowly than in the young. Many psychological problems of old age are the result of environmental factors, such as inadequate income and diet, inactivity, lack of physical and mental stimulation, loneliness, and reduced sensory information.

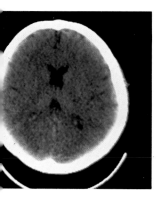
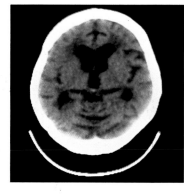

Left: Computerized brain scans of two subjects, a man of 30 and a man of 78. Darker areas show how brain tissue atrophies with age.

Right: Chart shows how the average weight of many organs drops as a function of age.

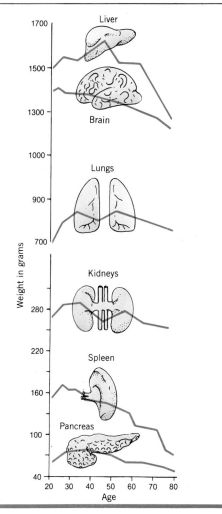

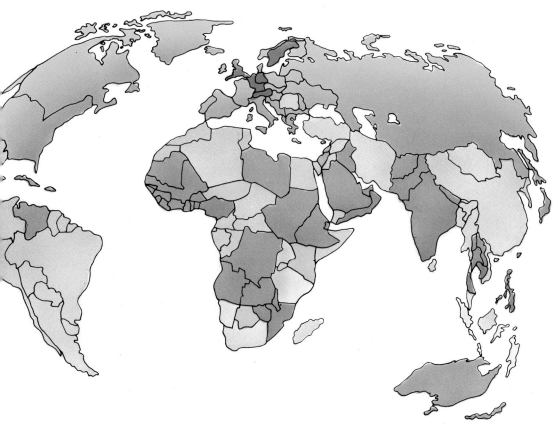

At the time of the Roman Empire, life expectancy was about 40 years. Only since the beginning of this century has that figure improved significantly; this is a result of a higher standard of living, better hygiene, and better health care.

The world map indicates with different colors the percentage of the population above 60 years of age. Countries in green have fewer than 5% above 60; in dark red, more than 20%.

According to estimates by UNESCO, in the year 2025 those countries marked in yellow will still have fewer than 5% of the population over age 60; countries in orange, above 20%.

Agricultural Machinery

The days of tough manual labor and horse-drawn equipment are over for many of the world's farmers. In the industrialized countries, agricultural production has become a highly mechanized science. Yet, even in this century, many farmers, accustomed to working the land with animals and their own hands, were often quite resistant to mechanization. Farming equipment did not really get on the technology bandwagon until the middle of the 19th century—a good 50 years after the Industrial Revolution had radically changed manufacturing techniques. Agricultural machinery grew more popular as technology improved and farming became less of a self-sufficient occupation and more of a massive, market-oriented operation. But it is only since the 1930s that mechanical power has largely re-

ment, making it possible automatically to adjust heights and angles on harrows, plows, and other implements. Thus, for example, farmers can set the depth to which they want the soil tilled. The power takeoff provides energy for machines that are either mounted on, or pulled by, the tractor. It empowers the moving parts of mowers, hay balers, combines, and spray pumps.

There are two basic types of tractors: the wheel tractor and the crawler. Today, 97 percent of all tractors used on farms are of the wheel variety. They are used primarily for seedbed preparation, cultivation, and pulling other machines. They often have very tall, powerful back wheels and smaller, sometimes closely spaced front wheels; this provides for good maneuverability between crop rows. Four-

Loosening the soil not only makes it easier for plants to root, it also increases the movement of air and water through the soil.

The plow is a primary tillage tool; it breaks up the crusty upper soil to a depth of 6 to 16 inches (15-40 cm). Usually pulled and powered by tractors, plows break up the soil by cutting, pushing, lifting, and inverting it. A tractor plow has from one to ten furrowing spades, called bottoms, which are attached to the frame. These bottoms have various shapes and cutting edges according to the sort of tillage and type of soil. The most common plow bottom for primary, or deep, tillage is the moldboard. It cuts in and inverts the furrow, burying the surface residue (including nutritious organic matter) as it tills. The moldboard plow bottom has

Large expanses of flat land permit high levels of mechanization, using large machines such as this experimental seeder.

Below: shaping the land is an essential step in cultivating it. Preparing a field for planting vegetables. The grooves in the soil are for irrigation.

placed manual and animal labor on farms in many areas.

Farm machinery comes in four basic varieties: power units, or tractors; soil-preparation, or tillage, machines; planters; and harvesters. These massive machines must be highly maneuverable and durable as well as precise and gentle in order to cultivate the land and harvest the crops.

Tractors

Tractors are the most useful all-purpose farm machines. Driven by gasoline or diesel engines, they act as power units and pulling devices for the more specialized seasonal equipment, such as plows and planters.

The basic tractor has several means of providing power to the implements attached to it. The drawbar is the device on the rear of the tractor frame to which machines such as plows and harrows are hitched. The hydraulic pump provides power to lift and lower attached equip-

wheel-drive tractors are now being introduced to provide better traction in difficult situations.

Crawler tractors are used for big, heavy jobs, such as land clearing, or where the ground is extremely rugged or soft. They have track wheels that look something like treaded conveyor belts in an endless loop, like those on army tanks.

Many modern tractors now have enclosed cabins, like trucks. They are sound- and shockproof and even climate-controlled. No longer do farmers have to bear inclement weather and bumpy riding conditions—they can concentrate solely on the work at hand.

Soil-Preparation Machinery

Plows, harrows, and cultivators are the basic machines for preplanting soil preparation. They make the land as hospitable as possible to plant life by tilling the earth into good seedbed material. Tillage helps plants take root and grow by mixing and loosening up the soil and uprooting weeds.

three main parts: the share, the landslide, and the moldboard. They are held together in a three-sided wedge shape by a frame called a frog. The share is the sharp cutting edge that slices the furrow section away from the ground. The moldboard, which lies above and behind the share, turns over the furrow, breaks it up, and pushes it to one side. Behind the share point is the landslide, which slides along the bottom of the cut furrow and keeps the plow steady as it works, absorbing the side thrust of the turning action.

Tillage machines that cut and shatter the soil without inverting it are known as field cultivators. They commonly have a series of slender, forklike shanks that rake through the soil. Field cultivators can cover an area of up to 60 feet (18 m) wide in just one pass. They have become progressively popular in preparing grain fields

The table shows the time required to plow 1 hectare of land (about 2.2 acres) at different levels of agricultural mechanization. The essential technique, cutting the soil into furrows with the blade, or share, of a plow, has not changed. What is different is the level of energy input.

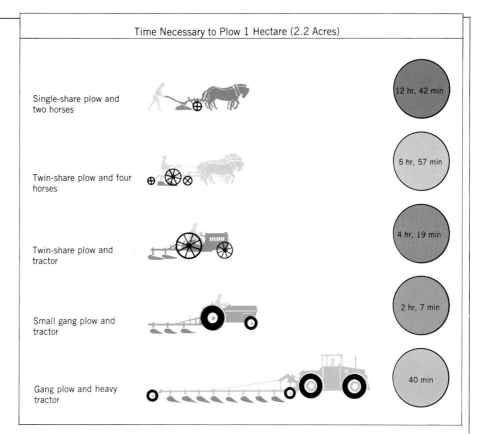

Time Necessary to Plow 1 Hectare (2.2 Acres)

Single-share plow and two horses		12 hr, 42 min
Twin-share plow and four horses		5 hr, 57 min
Twin-share plow and tractor		4 hr, 19 min
Small gang plow and tractor		2 hr, 7 min
Gang plow and heavy tractor		40 min

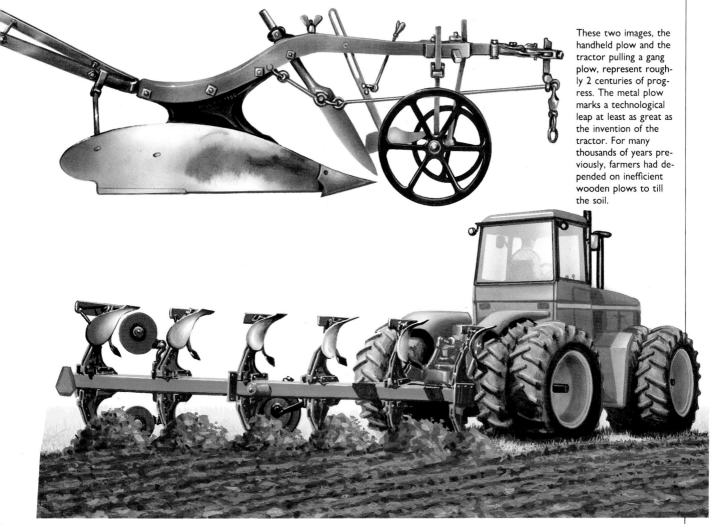

These two images, the handheld plow and the tractor pulling a gang plow, represent roughly 2 centuries of progress. The metal plow marks a technological leap at least as great as the invention of the tractor. For many thousands of years previously, farmers had depended on inefficient wooden plows to till the soil.

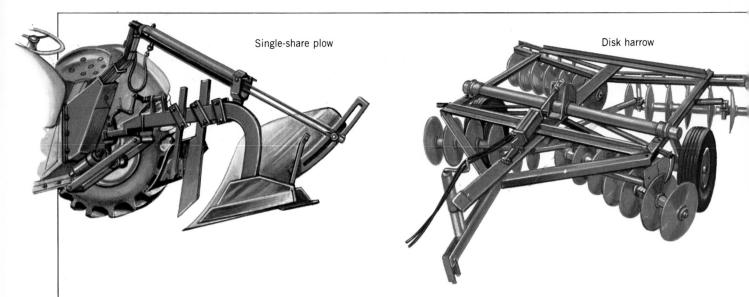

Single-share plow

Disk harrow

for planting. These cultivators leave more plant matter on the surface than plows and thereby reduce erosion. The trend in recent years has been toward this sort of light cultivation, because in most cases it is energy- and time-efficient and better for soil protection.

Primary cultivation is followed by harrowing, a process that breaks up the thick, sticky clods of earth that result from plowing. A harrow has sharp steel teeth or rounded disks that shatter these chunks of earth and smooth and level the seedbed's surface. Fertilizer, pesticide, and herbicide (weed-killer) dispensers are sometimes attached to the harrow.

Planting Machines

For centuries, seed was sowed by hand, but today, most field crops are planted by machines called drills. Drills have either forklike attachments that tear open furrows or rolling disks that open slits in the seedbed. They also have a series of seed dispensers, which deposit the seeds into each furrow or slit, and another device that immediately covers them with soil. Drills can plant over 12 rows of seed at once. Many drills are so wide that they are built to fold up in order to cross roadways. With modern seed drills, it is no longer necessary to plant twice the desired amount of

seeds and then go through the painstaking job of thinning out the underdeveloped plants. These amazing machines can seed at such precise depth and spacing that just about every plant is assured a healthy survival.

Harvesting Machines

Harvesting is done by a vast array of specialized equipment. Combines are used to harvest most grain and seed crops. A combine has several jobs to do. First, it

cuts the plant stalks, or stems. Then, it thrashes, or separates the grain from the straw. The combine leaves the waste straw on the ground while it collects up the grain and blows or augers it into a holding tank. When the tank is full, the grain is then augered to wagons or trucks for transport to storage. Many modern combines are no longer pulled by a tractor but are self-propelled. In fact, self-propelled equipment of all kinds is becoming increasingly popular among farmers. It allows for better

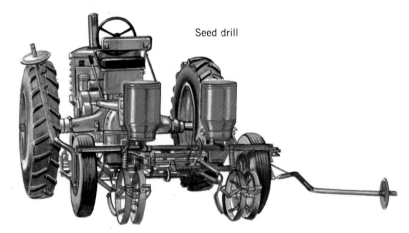

Seed drill

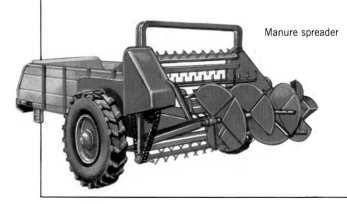

Manure spreader

Sprayer for fruit trees

As the selection of agricultural machines on these two pages suggests, nearly every step of raising a crop, from plowing and tilling to seeding and applying insecticides to harvesting and storage, is subject to mechanization.

Still, where the crop to be harvested is particularly delicate, as is the case with many kinds of fruit, human musclepower still has a role.

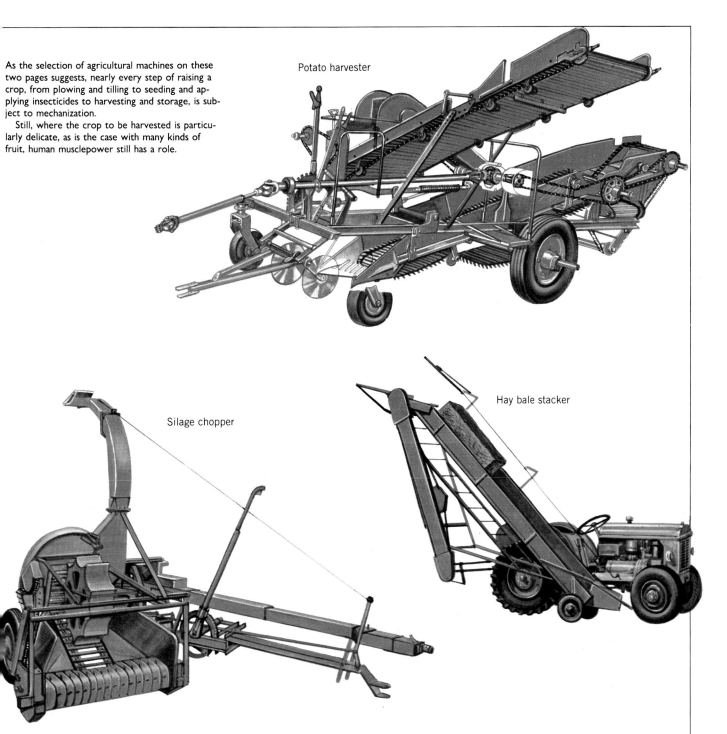

Potato harvester

Silage chopper

Hay bale stacker

maneuverability, higher speeds, and less fuel expense.

Another harvest machine is the corn picker-sheller, which snaps off the ears, removes the husks, and shells the grain from the cobs—all in one quick process. Hay-harvesting used to be a back-breaking job of mowing, raking, and stacking by hand and horse power. Now, all handwork has been eliminated as tractors and machinery are used for all operations. More and more farm machines that can do

many things at once are being developed. Such machines cut down expensive labor costs.

Farm machinery has come a long way since the first human-pulled wooden sticks that "plowed" the fields over 8,000 years ago. A modern farmer does very little agricultural work by hand. He must be a master of machinery. The newest agricultural equipment has enormous amounts of horsepower. For example, a mere 30 years ago, 30-horsepower tractor engines were

considered marvels; present-day tractors can run to over 300 horsepower. Modern farm machines have sophisticated hydraulics that save energy and provide better control. Many machines are self-monitoring and can be adjusted for maximum efficiency. Readouts in the cabin compartment tell the driver everything from engine speed to gasoline consumption to precisely how many seeds are being planted per field.

Agriculture

According to ancient writers, the legendary Chinese emperor Shen Nung was the inventor of agriculture. His subjects ate nothing but beef and wildfowl, but there were so many of them that they could not find enough animals to feed on. To keep his people from starving, Shen Nung carved one piece of wood into a plow-share (the blade of a plow), then bent another piece to make a handle. He taught his countrymen how to use the plow to grow millet, a kind of grain that conveniently fell to Earth from heaven when the emperor needed it.

Digging up the remains of ancient settlements, archaeologists have uncovered the real story. About 10,000 years ago, the men and women in Shen Nung's Yellow River valley, lived, like the rest of mankind, by hunting animals and gathering fruit, grain, and nuts. These hunters and gatherers existed in small, wandering bands that took food when they found it and then moved on. This was the way of life for most people throughout almost all of human history, and is still practiced by tiny groups in isolated places today.

Hunters and gatherers lived a relatively good life, but without refrigeration, they could not store food for a rainy day. There were good seasons and bad. In time of drought, what could you do? Furthermore, almost everywhere in the world, they kept facing the same problem—children. If any nomadic band had too many children, it became difficult to find enough animals and plants to feed everybody. Various groups limited the number of children by regulating sex, by abortion, or by killing babies outright; if they did not, the band would have to divide or people would die. The problem of overpopulation was solved, at least for a few thousand years, when an unknown north-ern Chinese genius started to grow her own food.

Basic Agriculture

Many anthropologists think it likely that the person who invented farming was a woman, since women were primarily responsible for gathering edible seeds. Whatever the inventor's sex, she or he discovered that if you plant a lot of seeds in a small area, you can produce more food yourself than if you simply go around gathering what grows in nature.

This discovery was independently made in many different areas—the Egyptian Nile Delta, the Amazon River valley in Brazil, western Pakistan, and what is now Turkey, among others—and archaeologists argue among themselves about which area was first. They agree, however, that, scientifically speaking, all agricultural systems work in the same way: Agriculture is the practice of establishing artificial ecosystems to feed human beings.

An ecosystem is a more or less balanced community of plants and animals, such as are found in lakes, forests, and plains. They are characterized by their stability, a condition usually ensured by natural mechanisms that prevent the population of any one species from becoming too abundant or scarce. Pine forests in the United States and Canada, for example, are prone to being choked by undergrowth. They are also frequently struck by lightning, which causes fires that threaten the forest. The lightning, however, burns away the brush. But the undergrowth tends to retain enough moisture to prevent lightning fires from spreading too far. Thus, the growth of plants and the effects of lightning strikes are balances, and the forest as a whole survives.

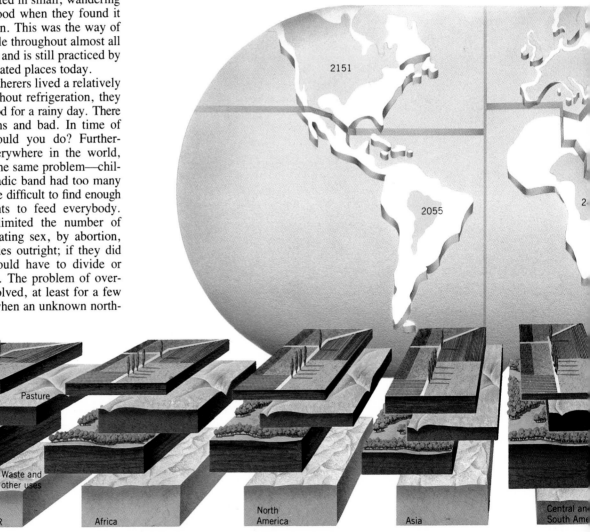

In developing countries, agriculture is a far more important source of income than in the developed world, where it does not usually exceed 3% of the gross national product.

The chart above shows the way land use varies from continent to continent. The figures on the world map indicate the land area in millions of hectares (1 ha = 2.2 a) given over to agriculture.

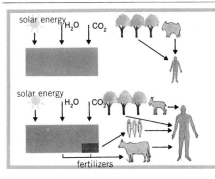

Before the agricultural revolution, game and wild crops fed about 10 million people. Today, 10% of the Earth's surface is under cultivation and feeds about 4,000 million people.

Man consumes some crops directly, others by way of animals that transform them first into meat and dairy products.

When people farm, they remove a section of land from a natural ecosystem and use their labor and the products of technology to create an artificial one. An essential difference between constructed and wilderness ecosystems is that people consume—literally eat up—part of the artificial system as food, and thus must use labor and technology as a substitute for what is removed. Ecosystems, broadly speaking, tend to cycle energy and nutrients among their various parts; when we take out some of that energy in the form of food, we have to put it back in some other way. That other way is the art and practice of farming.

There are two major divisions in farming: crop raising (cultivating plants) and animal husbandry (domesticating animals like cows, sheep, and goats). Most farms are mixtures of the two, although in this century of increasing specialization in agriculture, modern farms concentrate on one or the other.

Since the dawn of agriculture, most farms have combined plant and animal farming in an area less than 200 acres (81 ha) in size. This is still true for the majority of the world's population; more than half of all human beings farm relatively small plots. (The figure is much lower, usually less than 10 percent, for European and North American nations.) This article deals primarily with crop farming; domesticated animals are treated in ANIMAL HUSBANDRY.

Raising crops is not too different in principle from what Shen Nung showed his people. Essentially, you place seeds into a hole you have scratched in the earth and wait for them to grow. The kinds of seeds planted and the ways they are tended vary greatly from place to place. The best explanation of these differences lies in the kind of natural ecosystem the local farmers are replacing.

Types of Farming

In the Brazilian rain forest, for example, the reddish soil does not hold nutrients well. The essential minerals that plants need to take from the earth are readily washed out by the region's heavy rains. The thick jungle, however, acts as a canopy to protect the soil from the rainfall. In addition, the sheer amount of plant life retains nutrients by taking them up as soon as they become available.

The Indians of this area still practice what is known as slash-and-burn agriculture. They move into a thick jungle area and clear it by burning everything down. Then they quickly plant small amounts of dozens of different kinds of crops; a single half-acre (0.2 ha) plot might have as many as a hundred plant types. The tangled result looks like no farmland most Westerners have ever seen. After tending the land for a few years, the Indians abandon it and move on to burn away another section of the jungle.

For a long time, Europeans thought this method of cultivation was backward and harmful to the land. It was only recently discovered how well, in fact, it suits the jungle environment. The scores of different crops covering the same small plot created an artificial jungle that worked more or less like the real one, keeping nutrients from being lost in the soil. And burning down the jungle created the fertilizer—the ashes—necessary for the new crops to grow.

A totally different kind of artificial ecosystem was developed in China and Southeast Asia. The cultures that live there are sometimes called hydraulic civilizations because of their intensive use of irrigation and other systems of distributing

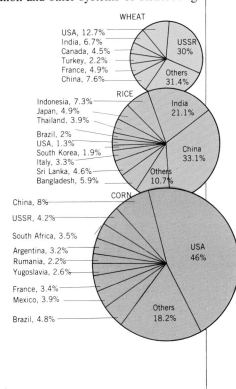

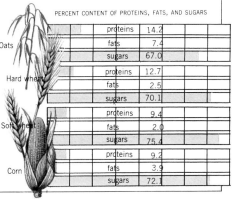

PERCENT CONTENT OF PROTEINS, FATS, AND SUGARS

Oats	proteins	14.2	
	fats	7.4	
	sugars	67.0	
Hard wheat	proteins	12.7	
	fats	2.5	
	sugars	70.1	
Soft wheat	proteins	9.4	
	fats	2.0	
	sugars	75.4	
Corn	proteins	9.2	
	fats	3.9	
	sugars	72.1	

Right: The three pie charts show the way world production of three important food crops is divided among different nations. The graph indicates the nutritional content of various food grains.

water. The way of life in a hydraulic civilization is an example of the complicated way in which the type of agriculture in an area affects the most intimate details of its people's existence.

Southeast Asia and China have many large river systems that provide abundant water for rice growing. Originally developed in India, rice farming is one of the most productive kinds of plant cultivation known. By the 11th century, varieties of quickly ripening rice had been discovered, and in only a few centuries their use had spread throughout China, Japan, Indochina, and Malaysia. The consequences for the population in these regions were dramatic. Great cities and organized government and religion are all evidence of a successful agricultural science.

Rice can be grown in small shallow lagoons called paddies, which get their water from rainfall and local rivers. In most ways, these 2-foot-deep (61-cm) pools reproduce the stable ecosystem of a marsh or river delta. The river provides a source of nutrients to the rice plants, which in turn tend to anchor the bottom with their roots. Diseases and weeds are prevented by intensive human labor; in some places, such as parts of Bali and Vietnam, rice is literally cultivated stalk by stalk, with people plucking out sickly plants as they come upon them.

All these types of plant farming had one thing in common: They were varieties of subsistence farming, agriculture that provided for the needs of the farmers themselves and the landlord, if there was one. There was usually little surplus left over to take to the market. Among other things, this meant that small-scale farmers were not much affected by the vicissitudes of the outside world. In revolutionary Iran, to cite a recent example, the 90 percent of the population that lived by subsistence farming were initially not much affected by the convulsions of political life.

This relation changes if farmers begin to grow cash crops, that is, goods to sell on the market. Instead of producing all the necessities of life on a single bit of land, the farmer specializes in a small number of crops, figuring that the money he receives from selling them will more than offset the expense of purchasing food he did not grow. Growing cash crops depends on having enough specialized knowledge and equipment to make this decision possible, as well as having clear economic methods of both selling produce and keeping the profits. These prerequisites all occurred throughout the world in various ways, but only in Europe, the United States and Canada, and parts of southern Asia did the peculiar

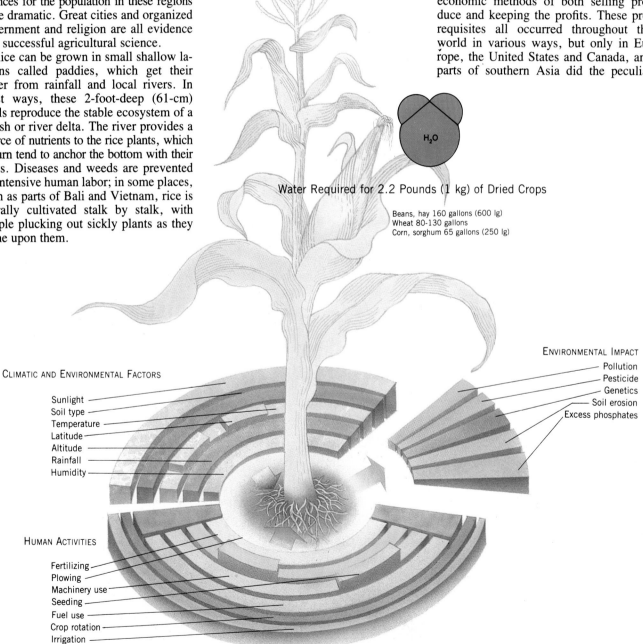

H$_2$O

Water Required for 2.2 Pounds (1 kg) of Dried Crops

Beans, hay 160 gallons (600 lg)
Wheat 80-130 gallons
Corn, sorghum 65 gallons (250 lg)

ENVIRONMENTAL IMPACT
— Pollution
— Pesticide
— Genetics
— Soil erosion
— Excess phosphates

CLIMATIC AND ENVIRONMENTAL FACTORS
Sunlight
Soil type
Temperature
Latitude
Altitude
Rainfall
Humidity

HUMAN ACTIVITIES
Fertilizing
Plowing
Machinery use
Seeding
Fuel use
Crop rotation
Irrigation

nation scientific team sponsored by the Rockefeller Foundation in Mexico. Borlaug's group developed high-yield, disease-resistant, low-chaff strains of wheat, maize (corn), and rice, and he was eventually awarded the 1970 Nobel Peace Prize for his efforts.

The results of Borlaug's work sparked what is known as the green revolution, an enormous upheaval that in the 1950-80 period transformed many Third World nations. Old crops were replaced by new ones, and new methods to grow them were taught, including irrigation and the use of petroleum-based artificial fertilizers. The high productivity of the green revolution crops made it possible for many farmers in Southeast Asia, India, and Latin Amer-

ica to grow cash crops, a move that was necessary if they were to pay for seeds, fertilizer, and irrigation. In this way, many thousands of remote villages were abruptly hooked into the worldwide economy; the changes were astonishing and often painful. People traded their self-sufficiency for access to the rest of the globe, a bargain some social scientists feel was not worth making.

The surge in agricultural knowledge had even more dramatic effects in the industrialized nations, especially in the United States and Canada, where the new techniques were accompanied by the introduction of a wide variety of farm machinery. In areas like the U.S. Midwest, the combination of Borlaug's crops

Of the many factors that affect soil fertility, most important is the amount of water available. Another key element is the organic material in the soil. Worms, bacteria, and other microorganisms break these substances down into useful plant nutrients. The chart opposite (bottom right) shows the relative populations of these organisms in healthy soil.

Below: Profiles of four common soil types. *A* and *B* are typical of the temperate zones. *C*, a poor type called *podzol*, is found in cold, humid zones like the Russian *taiga*. *D* shows the soil structure of tropical rain forests.

combination of political, social, and technological developments enable cash-crop agriculture to come into full flower.

In the West, the development of extensive legal codes regulating who owned land made it possible for individual small peasants to grow single crops and sell them at markets without having to divide the proceeds. In addition, the rapid growth of horticulture, the science of gardening, meant that farmers could apply particular techniques to special crops. As cultivators became less self-sufficient, they had to develop better growing techniques to keep ahead of their competitors.

Agribusiness

A combination of competitive pressure and a growing awareness of the problem of world hunger sparked intense scientific research during the 1930s and 1940s into the fields of plant genetics, pathology and physiology, entomology (the study of insects, particularly those that prey on crops), soil fertility, and the biochemistry of grains. One of the most important research efforts was led by U.S. agronomist Norman Borlaug, who directed a 17-

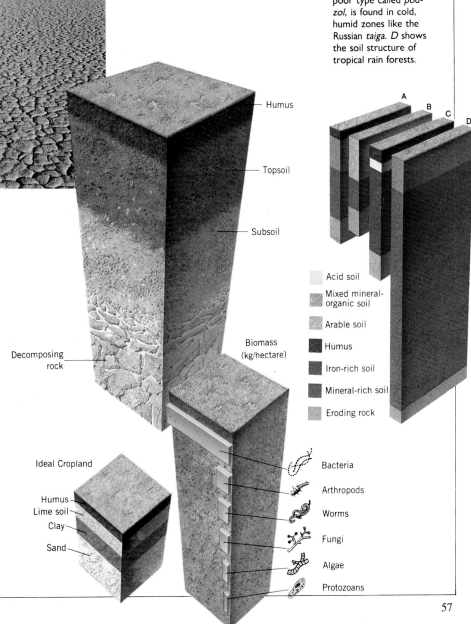

Humus

Topsoil

Subsoil

Decomposing rock

Biomass (kg/hectare)

Ideal Cropland

Humus
Lime soil
Clay
Sand

Acid soil

Mixed mineral-organic soil

Arable soil

Humus

Iron-rich soil

Mineral-rich soil

Eroding rock

Bacteria

Arthropods

Worms

Fungi

Algae

Protozoans

and the mechanization of agriculture meant that for the first time in history a small number of people (aided by a large number of machines) could grow a lot of food. Green revolution crops and heavy machinery work most efficiently on large tracts of land, because the cost per acre of both is lower; the result was the emergence of agribusiness, or corporate farming.

Although there were many exceptions, it is generally true that, in the past, farms became less productive per acre if they became too big. A large amount of land under cultivation simply could not be tended well unless many people worked the fields. Even when there were enough farm workers, they tended to be either slaves or near slaves, who had little reason to work well, or collective farmers, who rarely labored intensively because, although rewarded for their work, they did not personally see the results of their efforts. Thus, throughout human history, most productive farming was done on relatively small parcels of land.

Agribusiness changed all this. By using machines, a small group of people could plow and harvest thousands of acres. Whereas many men and women had formerly been required to weed and fertilize the land, a single pilot in a small plane could spray pesticides and nutrients onto huge tracts. Two or three people driving combines and threshers could reap an area in a few days that had in the past taken hundreds of field workers much longer.

In addition, substituting machines for farm animals dramatically changed the amount of land needed for farming. Before World War I, 91 million of the 3,330 million cultivated acres (1,350 million ha) in the United States were used to supply feed for the horses and mules that pulled the plows and hauled the harvests. Furthermore, almost a tenth of all farm workers employed were taking care of these horses and mules. Eliminating these animals dramatically cut the number of people and the amount of land needed for farming at the same time that other techniques were making the remaining cropland more productive and less labor-intensive. (Labor-intensive production is production that requires proportionally more human input than land or other resources.)

Ecologists, scientists who study ecosystems, call any ecosystem dominated by the presence of a single plant or animal a monoculture. Monocultures are inherently less balanced than ecosystems with many species, because the entire environment depends on the fortunes of one type of plant or animal. Rice paddies are something of an exception to this rule when they are supervised intensely, be-

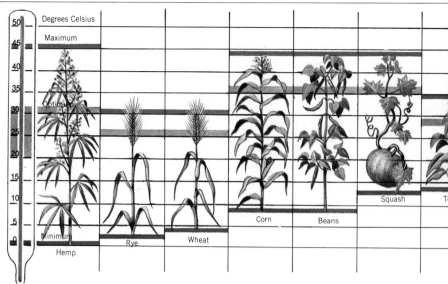

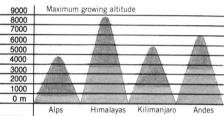

Climate, latitude, and altitude affect the choice of crops to be raised. The chart shows the temperature range within which common crops will grow.

cause human beings act to ensure that the system functions at optimum conditions. People keep the water supply constant by elaborate irrigation networks and watch over every rice plant.

The drawback is that this system requires enormous amounts of labor. Unlike hunting and gathering societies, hydraulic civilizations function better with many people in them, because the rice paddies can be better supervised. In addition, establishing the rice paddies in hilly areas required the construction of steplike terraces to prevent the water from running off—a process that also demanded huge amounts of human labor. The result is that small-scale rice farmers tend to have many children to help them in the fields. Although it is difficult to say either that rice farming encourages population growth or that growing populations in that part of the world encourage hydraulic agriculture, it is true that this kind of farming has had profound effects on the society.

Peasant Farming

Midway between these two extremes is traditional European peasant farming, which exists in its pure form in parts of southern Italy, Spain, and Portugal, in parts of Latin America, and in sections of the southern United States. Like rice-growing Asians, Europeans traditionally cultivated small, fixed plots of land. But like the practitioners of slash-and-burn agriculture, they generally grew many kinds of crops on their land. A typical

French peasant in the medieval era might have about 30 acres (12 ha) of land divided into several separate fields. The family would grow grapes on raised tables called vine arbors; a few olive trees; wheat, barley, millet, or some other kind of grain; hay for animals; and garden foods like turnips or beans. Many common foods such as the tomato and potato were then unknown, since they originated in the New World.

Unlike slash-and-burn farmers, medieval peasants did not generally cultivate their various crops on the same land but, rather, set aside small portions of land for each. Although one species might not grow well in a particular year, there were usually enough other kinds of crops for something to do well. Further, farmers usually practiced crop rotation—that is, a single piece of land might be planted with wheat one year, clover the next, and remain fallow (unused) the third. Crop rotation ensured that intensive cultivation of a single crop with specific requirements in one parcel of land would not exhaust particular nutrients in that land.

Corporate Farming

Small-scale farmers traditionally grow several crops on their land. Corporate farmers, by contrast, specialize by purchasing bulk quantities of one variety of, say, genetically improved wheat. Perhaps 2,000 acres (810 ha) or more are set aside for that year's wheat crop and plowed by large tractors. The field is then fertilized, either by spraying nitrogen-rich chemi-

FOUR-YEAR CROP ROTATION

	Past	Present
	Plowing 13 h 42 m	1 hr 14 m
Corn	Disking 2 h	40 m
Wheat	Harrowing 1 h 56 m	24 m
Clover	Seeding 1 h 22 m	32 m
	Cover seeds 1 h 8 m	
	Cutting 2 h 1 m	
	Stacking 16 h	
	Winnowing 15 h	39 m
	53 hours, 9 minutes	3 hours, 29 minutes

New hybrid seeds can double or triple crop yield, but such heavy use can also wear out croplands. Pesticides and insecticides disturb soil ecosystems. As a result, crop rotation is more necessary than ever to give the soil a chance to rest and recover fertility.

The chart on the right shows how increasing mechanization has cut the time required to raise and harvest wheat.

cals from the air or by using a gas fertilizer machine, a motorized vehicle that forces nutrients into the soil through pipes.

After the wheat is planted, the field is periodically sprayed to kill insect pests. Much has been written about the long-term harm of pesticides, and researchers are intensively working on other methods of controlling insects and blights. To water the crop if natural rainfall is not enough, the land may be irrigated by digging a channel or laying a pipe to a nearby body of water. On large farms, fields are watered by using quarter-mile-long pipes mounted on wheels. Machines roll the pipe to a desired location, and sprinklers spray the water.

After the Sun ripens the wheat, it is harvested by a thresher, a complicated,

tractorlike vehicle that simultaneously cuts the plants and shakes them to separate the grain from the rest. The small grains of wheat fall through holes in a screen and into a bin in the thresher, while the rest of the plant is ejected out the back. Similar devices called combines are used for peas and beans; a pea combine can harvest almost half a ton of peas before it has to be emptied.

Machines have been devised to mechanically harvest crops that it would not seem possible to harvest without hand labor. Corn threshers, for example, snap off the stalk and then use mechanical "hands" to feel along the plant until they come to an ear. The ear is picked, and the rest of the stalk is thrown away. Mechanical potato harvesters use scoops to pull up po-

tato plants, which are then tumbled about to separate the edible tuber from the rest of the plant and from clinging soil.

Crop remains—the chaff, cornstalks, bean stems, or potato leaves—are sometimes plowed into the soil. More mechanized farms, however, use balers to bundle up suitable residues for fodder, or animal feed. The balers are the same automatic devices that scoop up and pack cut hay. The fodder is stored in a silo, where it is converted by fermentation to silage, which can keep for months.

Running a modern mechanized farm is a demanding task that requires a great deal of specialized knowledge. Further, the huge amount of money needed to buy the equipment and land means that modern farmers must in addition borrow thou-

The overuse of pesticides can lead to the elimination of useful organisms as well as the pests. There is concern, too, that heavy use of herbicides cuts genetic variety in the plant kingdom by indiscriminately destroying any plant not immediately useful.

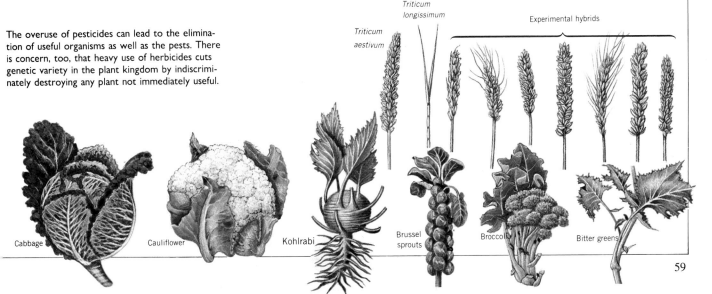

Triticum aestivum

Triticum longissimum

Experimental hybrids

Cabbage   Cauliflower   Kohlrabi   Brussel sprouts   Broccoli   Bitter greens

sands of dollars at a time. As farms become larger and more specialized, the risks increase as well. If the bean crop failed on a medieval peasant's small farm, he had many other crops to rely on. A modern farmer who has sunk his fortune into growing hundreds of acres of beans would be in serious financial trouble in case of one-crop failure.

Most industrial countries with strong agribusiness communities have evolved complicated legislative packages to protect corporate farmers. When in good years agribusiness's enormous productivity drives prices down to an unacceptable level, nations such as the United States have subsidy programs to buy crops at guaranteed prices. Other types of subsidies give producers of some kinds of agricultural commodities—cotton and tobacco, for example—tax breaks, investment incentives, and protective tariffs. Still other programs pay farmers not to grow certain crops because their overproduction would cause prices to fall.

Agribusiness is the most efficient way ever discovered to grow food. But critics of agribusiness charge that its heavy reliance on petroleum-based fertilizers, increasingly potent pesticides, and genetically manipulated stocks of seed in fact makes the entire agricultural system unstable. According to this view, the diversity of small farms in the past protected them from being hurt if any one

crop failed. If a blight attacks a modern wheat farm, on the other hand, it can wreak enormous damage. Agribusiness, in short, puts all the farmer's eggs in one basket, as questionable a practice in agriculture as it is in anything else.

Agribusiness supporters point to the system's high productivity and say that

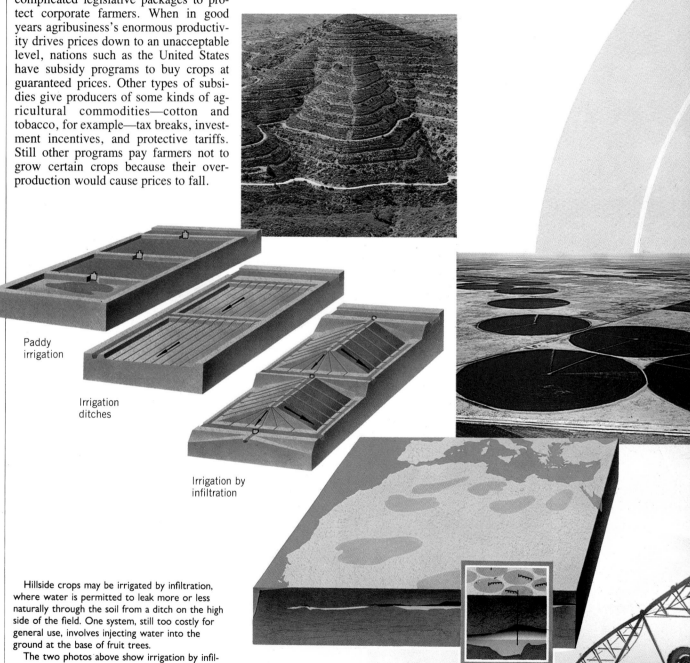

Paddy irrigation

Irrigation ditches

Irrigation by infiltration

Hillside crops may be irrigated by infiltration, where water is permitted to leak more or less naturally through the soil from a ditch on the high side of the field. One system, still too costly for general use, involves injecting water into the ground at the base of fruit trees.

The two photos above show irrigation by infiltration in Cyprus and the result of rotating sprinkler systems in the Libyan desert. The streams from these self-powered mobile sprinklers like the one illustrated, right, may be several miles long. This form of irrigation produces good results in desert regions, drawing on underground lakes for water supply. After a few years, though, the desert soil, poor in organic materials, loses its fertility.

Irrigation opens otherwise infertile arid land to cultivation. It may also be necessary where there is rainfall, but not when it is needed. The method of irrigation chosen depends on whether the land is flat or hilly and on the crop. Rice requires seasonal flooding, vegetables are often watered by ditches between the rows, and other field crops may do best with sprinkler systems.

simple carefulness will be enough to avert
any possible disasters. For a world full of
hunger, they say, there is no other solution. In either case, agribusiness is likely
to persist for some time, a remote successor to the simple plowing legendarily at-
tributed to the Chinese emperor Shen
Nung.
See also FERTILIZER; PESTICIDE.

Transport robot

Control box

Robot cultivating strip fields

Storage

ROBOT CROP CULTIVATION

Increasing agricultural mechanization suggests that
many fields will eventually be cultivated entirely by
robots. Such fields will probably take the form of
long strips.
Top: Mechanized cotton harvesting in the
United States.

Air Conditioner

Late in the 19th century, the earliest air conditioners—crude and bulky machines by today's standards—were invented to control humidity in textile plants. Little did those enterprising factory engineers realize that their invention would become one of the fundamental features of the 20th century. As early as 1922, a building was air-conditioned solely for human comfort (it was a movie theater, of course). Within three decades, air conditioning had become commonplace in many homes and places of business around the world.

We tend to think of air conditioning simply as a means of keeping homes and offices cool during hot weather. It does this, of course, but it accomplishes much more. Air conditioners are mechanical devices that maintain air temperature, control humidity (the amount of water vapor in the air), remove dust, pollen, and other particulate matter from air, and keep the air circulating. There are centralized air conditioning plants that cool (and heat) 100-story office buildings, and there are small air conditioning units that cool a single room. The single-room unit is a good example of how air conditioners work.

On the near right is a sealed compressor unit from a household refrigerator. It liquefies the coolant gas that absorbs heat from the interior of the refrigerator. The gas then discharges heat from cooling fins, which are usually placed at the rear of the appliance.

On the opposite page are (top) a cutaway diagram of a standard closed circuit air conditioning unit and (below) an exploded view of a similar device, showing the principal parts.

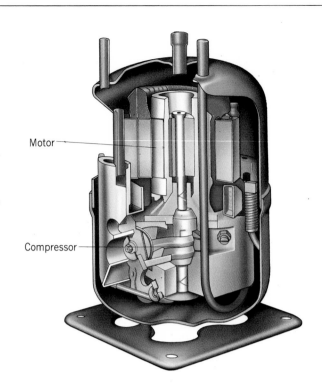

Motor

Compressor

The Single-Room Unit

The typical single-room wall unit is a box containing an electric motor, a compressor, several fans, and a closed system of tubing (including several sets of coils) that contains a refrigerant. (Refrigerants are chemical compounds that readily absorb heat—ice is a common, if short-lived, example.)

The central principle of refrigeration (and the basic operation accomplished by air conditioners) is heat transfer. To simplify, an air conditioner takes room air and "robs" it of its heat, then recirculates this cooler air through the room; the heat that is absorbed, meanwhile, is expelled through the part of the air conditioner that is outside the room. How is an air conditioner able to repeat this cycle again and again? By the use of a remarkable group of refrigerant compounds, usually of Freon.

Refrigerants

Freon is a synthetic compound of carbon and fluoride that fluctuates between liquid and gas within a range of temperatures typical of summer climate. It is odorless, colorless, noncorrosive, nonflammable, and generally not harmful—advantages that were absent in earlier refrigerants such as ammonia.

There are a number of formulations of Freon, depending on differing refrigeration tasks, and they all make good refrigerants, because they have high densities and low boiling points. Those are impor-

tant factors in the evaporator coils, which are coils filled with liquid Freon.

In its liquid state, Freon is very cold. When an air conditioner is running, the evaporator fan draws air from the room over the coils. The air is cooled as Freon rapidly absorbs its heat—so much so that with its low boiling temperature, Freon boils and becomes a gas just from the heat of a summer day. At the same time, air humidity is reduced because water vapor in the air condenses, or turns to liquid, on the cooler evaporator coils. In this way, air is both cooler and drier when it leaves an air conditioner than when it went in. It is also cleaner, because intake air is passed through a particulate filter.

The Compressor

The overheated Freon gas moves on through tubes that lead from the evaporator coils to the compressor, a mechanical chamber that increases the pressure (and thus the temperature) of a gas. The compressor also acts like a pump in that it forces Freon to move through an air conditioner's coils, whether in liquid or gaseous form.

From the compressor, Freon gas passes into the condenser coils. The condenser fan blows air from outdoors over these coils. The outside air may seem sticky and hot, but it is cool compared to the temperature of the Freon gas, which promptly surrenders its heat to the air; at this lower temperature, then, it will convert back into a liquid upon depressurization.

This depressurization is accomplished when the Freon passes through a capillary tube, which becomes increasingly narrow and has the effect of reducing pressure. At this lower pressure, Freon becomes positively chilly—and condenses. It then reenters the evaporator coils, and the cycle of heat exchange is complete. As long as your air conditioner is humming (or groaning, as the case may be), this cycle is continuous. Because of Freon's dramatic temperature changes, it goes from cold to boiling and back to cold in a very short time, and all within a single tube that snakes around the interior of a standard window unit.

In central air conditioning, the air is filtered, cooled, and dehumidified in one central plant, then circulated through a home, building, or factory through ducts. Controlled air quality is essential to the production of everything from watches to munitions and to the efficient operation of large computers and thus is a prerequisite of many industrial, high-technology production and data processing systems.

How much "cool" does an air conditioner provide? An experiment at the University of Illinois during the 1930s suggests a possible answer. It showed that a two-story home used over 2 tons of ice (10 200-kg blocks) in a day. The air conditioner, everyone agrees, is more convenient.

See HEAT TRANSFER.

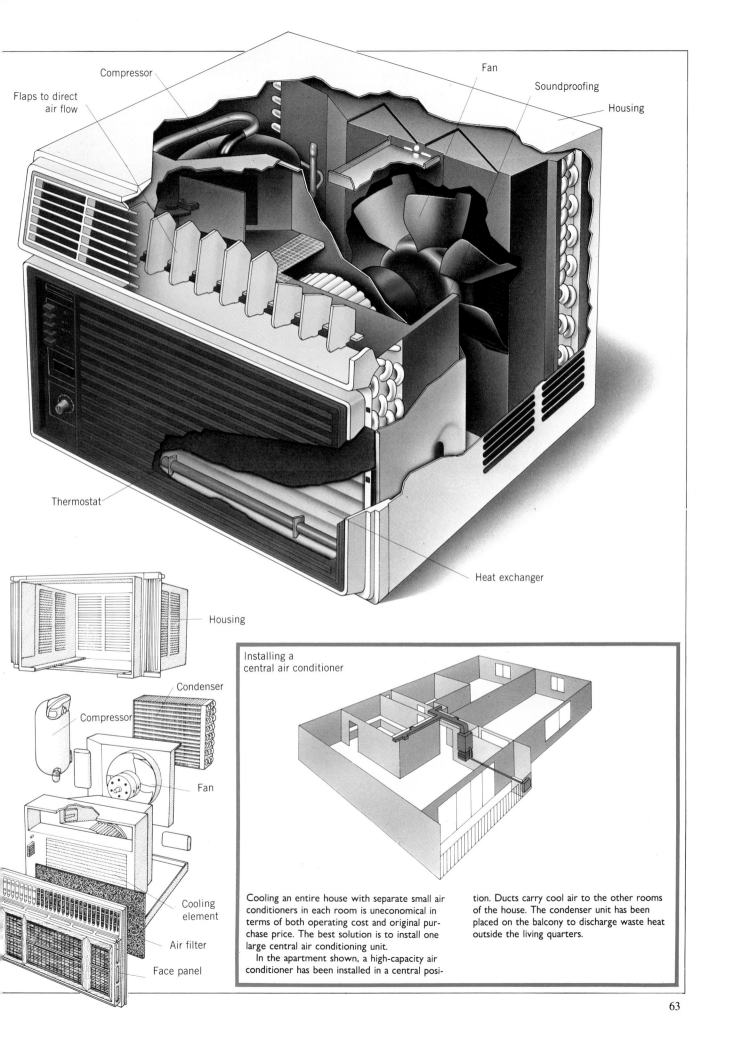

Compressor

Fan

Soundproofing

Housing

Flaps to direct
air flow

Thermostat

Heat exchanger

Housing

Condenser

Compressor

Fan

Cooling
element

Air filter

Face panel

Installing a
central air conditioner

Cooling an entire house with separate small air conditioners in each room is uneconomical in terms of both operating cost and original purchase price. The best solution is to install one large central air conditioning unit.

In the apartment shown, a high-capacity air conditioner has been installed in a central posi-tion. Ducts carry cool air to the other rooms of the house. The condenser unit has been placed on the balcony to discharge waste heat outside the living quarters.

Air Traffic Control

In the modern world, two sets of rules govern the flight of all aircraft. One is called VFR, for visual flight rules, and it governs flight under conditions of acceptable visibility—when the pilots can see where they are going and what other traffic may be in the vicinity. VFR conditions are prescribed and marked on aeronautical charts; they may vary from country to country or even from locality to locality.

IFR, for instrument flight rules, controls all flights under conditions of restricted visibility—in clouds, rain, snow, fog, and so on. Under IFR, actual control of the airplane passes from the pilot to a controller in a ground station equipped with a variety of complex instruments (chiefly radar). The air traffic controller observes the airplane's movements and by voice radio tells the pilot which speed, altitude, and course to fly while also warning him of other traffic in his vicinity.

To the pilot flying IFR, the sky may be a mass of grayish cotton-wool; to the ground controller, it is a radar screen filled with numerous yellow blips, each representing an airplane. Each airplane has attached to it a data block identifying it by number and giving its speed, altitude, and course. When two blips are on a converging course, the controller instructs one of them to change altitude or course or both, to avoid collision. If the airplane is in a terminal area and intends to land, the controller governs its flight all the way to touchdown on the runway, and sometimes beyond.

Terminal and En-Route Control

The two broad areas of air traffic control are terminal control areas and en-route control areas. Large and busy airports are covered, in effect, by a bubble of controlled airspace that may extend upward as far as 30,000 feet (9,150 m) and cover a circle 20 miles (32 km) or more in diameter. Within this bubble, flight is strictly controlled by instructions from the ground. Airplanes must be fully equipped with instruments required for IFR flying, and pilots must be instrument-rated—certified as to their qualifications for flying by instruments only. Controllers are required to keep all aircraft separated both horizontally and vertically by a specified distance.

En-route traffic control governs all flight between points of departure and arrival. Rules are designed to keep aircraft safely separated from the first point to the last, and to see that they are separated at such points of convergence as the radio beacons in the sky that mark en-route airways, where there are many changes in course. There are also specified points along the airways where a pilot is required to report to an ATC ground station

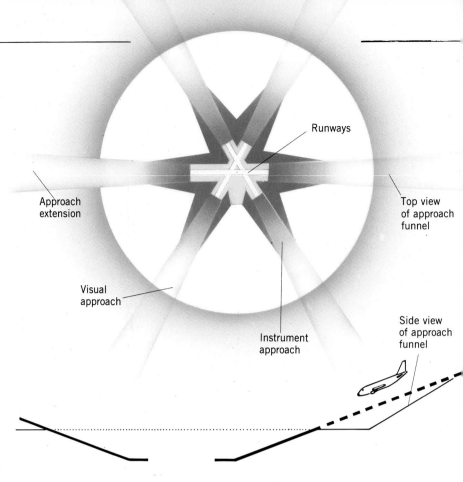

his altitude, speed, course, and time of passing, so that potentially dangerous convergence of courses can be foreseen and avoided.

"Separation" is a succinct way of describing the ground controller's job, whether at a terminal facility or an en-route station. Pilots, controllers, and everyone else involved in air traffic control must learn to think in three-dimensional terms—up and down, all around—and in terms of lead time. A jet may be overhauling a small plane ahead at four or five times the small plane's speed. The point of potential collision is miles away, but preventive measures must be taken immediately.

Equipment

To accomplish this, air traffic control systems have a variety of sophisticated machines and electronic systems. Transponders aboard aircraft automatically transmit identification, altitude, course, and speed for the data block on the ground radar screen. Radio beacons transmit navigational aids on 360 course radials, one for each point on the compass. Collision-alert systems foresee course convergences and issue warnings. Cockpit displays, as on a television screen, show the pilot approaching weather dangers. Engineers are working on automatic approach and landing systems that will guide an airplane from an approach point into the traffic

pattern of the destination airport, line the plane up with the runway, and bring it down to a pinpoint landing without the pilot's having to touch the controls.

There is also an advisory service connected with air traffic control that gives a pilot full information on weather and special conditions along his intended route. Such preflight briefings are available to all, even the smallest private plane, as are similar en-route briefings at specified checkpoints. About the only thing a pilot cannot do is fly any way he wants to. The old days of personal freedom in the air are over.

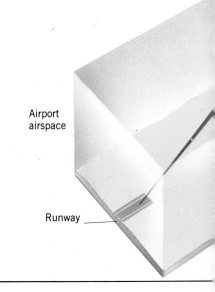

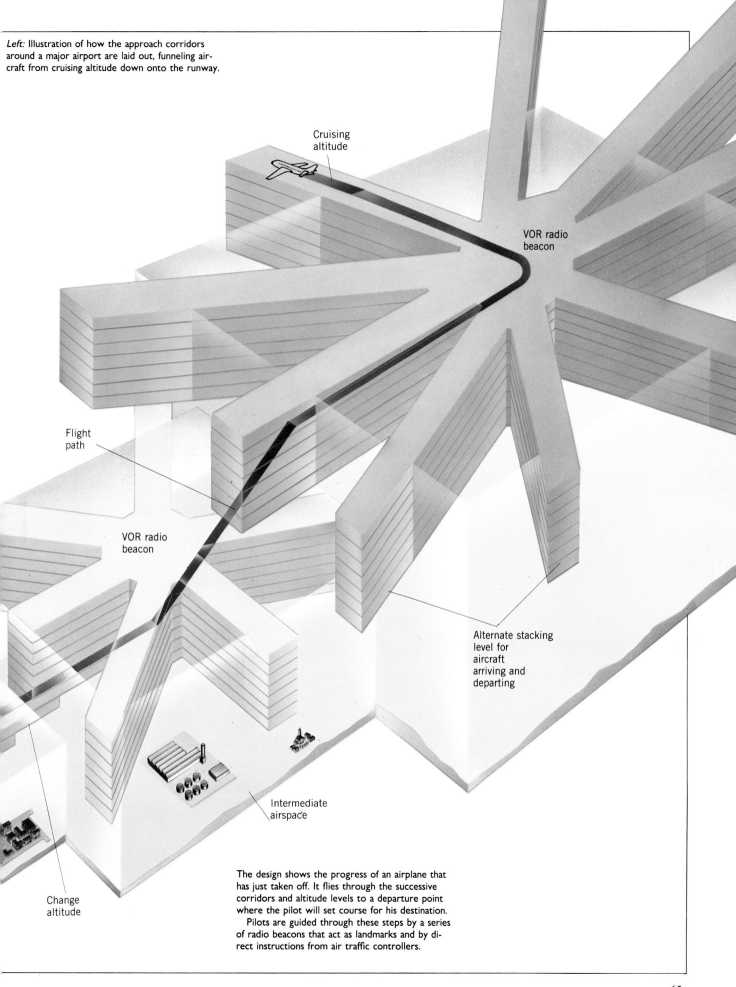

Left: Illustration of how the approach corridors around a major airport are laid out, funneling aircraft from cruising altitude down onto the runway.

Cruising altitude

VOR radio beacon

Flight path

VOR radio beacon

Alternate stacking level for aircraft arriving and departing

Intermediate airspace

Change altitude

The design shows the progress of an airplane that has just taken off. It flies through the successive corridors and altitude levels to a departure point where the pilot will set course for his destination.

Pilots are guided through these steps by a series of radio beacons that act as landmarks and by direct instructions from air traffic controllers.

Aircraft, Heavy Transport

. It is perhaps not surprising that the airplane in its early years was not thought of as a load carrier. Flimsy in construction and frail in engine power, the thrust of its early development, once it had proved itself in World War I, was all toward carrying passengers and transporting the mail. It took a second worldwide war, from 1939 to 1945, to demonstrate what extraordinary cargo-lifting tasks the airplane could perform over long routes. The air-transport route known as the Red Ball Express carried military cargo of all kinds from war plants in the United States through South America, across the South Atlantic, across Africa to India, and thence across the mountains known as the Hump, direct to combat lines in China and Burma.

These operations—and there were similar ones running westward—were carried out with military versions of familiar commercial planes: C-47s (the DC-3), C-54s (the DC-4), and others. After the war, air freight suddenly loomed as big business. In 1945, the Flying Tiger Line, then known as the National Skyway Freight Corporation, was set up, followed shortly by Seaboard & Western Airlines. Not long after, aircraft began to be specifically adapted and even built for this new type of flying service.

The most spectacular demonstration the world has ever had of what air transport can do came with the Berlin airlift of 1948-49. In a dispute over access from the west to that city of 3 million people, the Soviets had blocked roads, railroads, and canals. Gen. Lucius Clay, the American governor, replied by organizing every available American transport plane in Europe to supply Berlin by air; 24 hours per day, in an unending stream, the C-47s, C-46s, C-54s, and whatever other aircraft were available brought coal, food, gasoline, and even candy for the children, one plane landing approximately every 1½ minutes. And, in the end, the blockade was broken.

Just 10 years later, transport planes were available that could have handled the whole job with a fraction of the effort.

The Berlin airlift planes had a capacity of about 4 tons and a range of 1,500 miles (2,400 km); the Air Force C-141 jet transport in 1965 could carry 45 tons 3,000 miles (4,800 km). In 1970 the Lockheed C-5A, an airplane built for "global logistics," went into service with a load capacity of 110 tons that it could carry up to 3,700 miles (5,000 km). Ten C-5As alone, it was estimated, could have done the job of the entire Berlin airlift fleet.

A "Milestone" Airplane

As with the DC-3 and airline passenger service, there was a "milestone" airplane in the air freight business that showed what a good transport could do. This was the Douglas DC-8-63F, a conversion of the first Douglas jet airliner, the DC-8. Called the "Super Sixty DC-8," this was a lengthened version of the original airplane, whose capacious fuselage seemed made to order for large and heavy loads. The Flying Tiger Line put 19 of the Super Sixties in service, and business boomed.

The successor to the Super Sixty in the civilian air transport field was the Boeing 747, the first of the new generation of jumbo jets. Just as the 747 doubled the number of passengers that could be carried at that time, it doubled the weight of cargo. Stripped of everything save twin tracks of roller bearings for loading, the 747 cargo version looked, in the interior, like a storage shed for railroad cars rather than an airplane. It could load containerized freight of international standard dimensions comparable to those carried by trucks and rail cars, the first airplane to do so.

It is an astonishing fact that, today, there is scarcely anything that cannot be carried by air as safely, if more expensively, and—above all—faster, than by any other mode of transport. Armed forces can fly a whole division of troops, with all of their equipment and necessary logistical backup, to anywhere in the world. Organizations that deal in such huge and fragile things as booster space rockets can even send them by air to the launching pad, as was demonstrated in 1963 when a Boeing Stratocruiser was modified to carry rockets to Cape Kennedy. The plane was lengthened by 16 feet (5 m) and given a 20-foot-wide (6 m) cargo compartment. The resulting monstrosity was nicknamed the "Pregnant Guppy"; it carried the rockets and has subsequently carried components of the Airbus wide-body airliner, an international cooperative effort at airplane building, from Germany, Spain, and England to the assembly line in Toulouse, France.

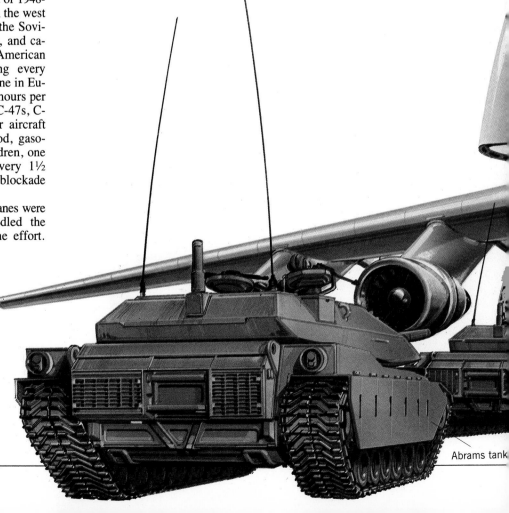

The gigantic Lockheed C-5 Galaxy, 69 feet (21 m) high at the tail, has a cargo capacity above 100 tons. The illustration shows the Galaxy being loaded with two Abrams heavy tanks.

Abrams tank

Messerschmitt ME-323; WW II, Germany; takeoff weight of 43.5 tons, powered by six motors of 1,000 horsepower each. It could carry 120 fully equipped soldiers or 60 wounded.

Savoia-Marchetti S.M.-82; WW II, Italy; 17.8 tons at takeoff, the S.M.-82 was powered by three 860-horsepower motors and could transport 5 tons of cargo or 28 soldiers for 1,900 miles (3,000 km), a record distance at the time.

Douglas C-133 Cargomaster; 1950s, USA. Four 6,500-horsepower piston engines permitted the plane to weigh 124 tons at takeoff and carry 200 soldiers or entire ballistic missiles for a distance of 3,975 miles (6,395 km).

Lockheed C-141 Starlifter, 1960s, USA. With a takeoff weight of 143 tons, four jet engines gave the Starlifter a 40-ton cargo capacity and a range of 6,450 miles (10,370 km).

Lockheed C-5 Galaxy, currently the world's largest aircraft. Takeoff weight is 348 tons, of which 100 is cargo. The Galaxy has a range of over 3,800 miles (6,000 km).

Ilyushin IL-76. This Russian transport has characteristics similar to those of the Lockheed C-141.

Beyond the Earth

The successful first flights of the U.S.-built space shuttle have demonstrated that air transport is ready to move beyond the Earth's surface and play its part in building a new future and new frontiers. Here is a plane that, for the first time, can move between two worlds, at home in each, opening a vista that seems endless.

Aside from the ability to carry heavy cargos for long distances, military transport aircraft must satisfy other rigid requirements. These are governed by the conditions they would meet in wartime. Hurriedly built combat airstrips, for instance, imply the need for specially reinforced landing gear and relatively short takeoff and landing distances.

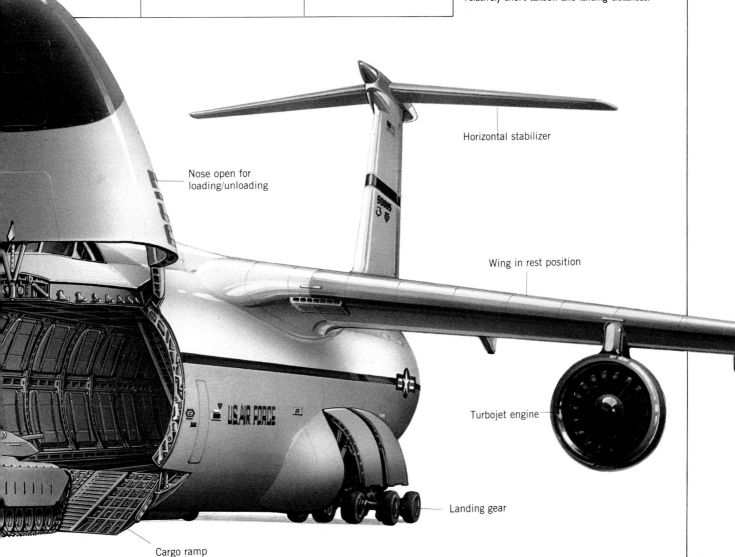

Nose open for loading/unloading

Horizontal stabilizer

Wing in rest position

Turbojet engine

Landing gear

Cargo ramp

Aircraft, Light Transport And STOL

Since the first day of their existence, one problem with airplanes has been that they need to run long distances on the ground to gain speed for takeoff or to lose speed after landing. This has resulted in the necessity of building airports outside of the cities that they serve, and this in turn has led to problems of transportation to the airports, to congestion and delay. Small wonder, then, that much time has been spent trying to find a way to get an airplane quickly and safely into the air—if possible, straight up.

The most obvious answer to the problem was the helicopter, but it was a long time in coming. The first nearly practical design was evolved by a Spaniard, Juan de la Cierva, in the 1920s. He built a hybrid helicopter-airplane, in which a large, free-spinning rotor replaced the airplane's wing. Since the rotor began to spin and therefore develop lift almost as soon as the airplane began to move, its takeoff run was very short. It landed by the same principle of autorotation. But though some 500 of these so-called "Autogyros" were built, largely for military purposes, a truly practical helicopter design was never developed from this promising beginning.

Flying Indoors

A German design, the Focke-Achgelis, took the Autogyro one step further in the late 1930s. It was the first fully controllable helicopter, as was demonstrated by the famous German woman pilot Hanna Reitsch, who in 1938 flew it inside the Deutschland Halle in Berlin. This machine had two rotors, one each on outriggers fastened to the fuselage of a conventional Stieglitz training airplane from which the wings had been removed. World War II slowed any further development, however, and it was not until Igor Sikorsky, the Russian-born designer, introduced his Vought-Sikorsky VS-300 in May 1940 that the helicopter was born.

The VS-300 was so successful that it was put immediately into production and saw military service, as the R-4, in Europe and the Pacific in 1944. By 1947 a commercial version, the S-51, was being experimented with by various airlines, and in 1952 a 12-passenger helicopter, the S-55, was certificated by the FAA and began carrying mail and passengers.

A Tilt for a Takeoff

More promising as a transport perhaps will be V/STOL (for Vertical/Short Take-Off and Landing) aircraft operating on the tilt-rotor, tilt-wing, and vectorable-nozzle principles. These types are under intensive development in several countries, notably the United States and Britain, which have jointly developed the success-

This Italian Aeritalia G-222 is executing a 'touch-and-go' parachute drop, discharging cargo without ever coming to a halt on the runway. A parachute drags the cargo down the open jump ramp. In practice, this kind of drop is often performed without touching the ground at all, flying at an altitude of 6 to 13 feet (2-4 m).

Douglas C-47 Skytrain or Dakota: Top speed of 230 miles (370 km) per hour with a range of 1,600 miles (2,574 km) and a cargo capacity of 8,800 pounds (4,000 kg) or 27 soldiers.

DeHavilland Canada DHC-5 Buffalo: Top speed of 168 miles (271 km) per hour with a range of 2,040 miles (3,280 km). Takeoff distance is 950 feet (290 m) with a cargo of 41 soldiers.

Aeritalia G-222: Top speed 335 miles (540 km) per hour with a range of 1,830 miles (2,950 km). Cargo capacity is 11,000 pounds (5,000 kg) or 44 soldiers.

Lockheed C-130 Hercules: Top speed 1,384 miles (618 km) per hour with a range of 2,500 miles (4,000 km). Transport capacity is 91 soldiers.

I.A.I. 201 Arava: Top speed 202 miles (326 km) per hour with a range of 800 miles (1,300 km). Takeoff distance is 950 feet (290 m) with a cargo capacity of 5,100 pounds (2,300 kg).

Antonov An-72, NATO code name Coaler: This Russian light transport has a top speed of 420 miles (680 km) per hour, a range of 2,000 miles (3,200 km) and can carry 32 soldiers.

ful Harrier series of military aircraft. For taking off, the jet engine's exhausts are rotated 90° so that their thrust is directed straight downward. Thus, the aircraft is lifted vertically, and, once aloft, the engines are rotated to the horizontal, giving the aircraft normal forward movement at jet-engine speeds of up to 600 miles (965 km) per hour.

Drawbacks to a commercial version of the principle are several. The noise at takeoff is deafening, and not much can be done to muffle it. The downward blast from the jet engines raises veritable hurricanes of dust, dirt, and flying debris, potentially harmful not only to passengers but also to the aircraft. And in the heart-stopping moment when the exhaust nozzles are being tilted from one position to another, there are problems of stability and control that would probably be unacceptable to airlines and the flying public.

The possibilities of increasing the efficiency of the fixed wing, by such devices as slots and flaps for shortened conventional takeoff and landing, have by no means been exhausted. Such mechanisms are not likely ever to make of a fast-cruising jet a slow-landing flying bus, but already impressive results have been achieved.

See also HELICOPTER; WING, AIRPLANE.

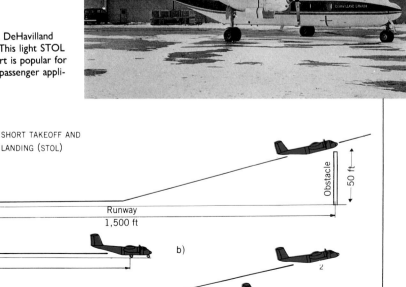

The key to the design of a STOL (Short Takeoff and Landing) aircraft is in the special aerodynamics of the wing, which is usually extra-long. The body of the aircraft is typically fat and squat, so as to accommodate a variety of cargos.

The chart below, right, shows the takeoff characteristics of STOL aircraft; its ability to overcome set obstacles in *a* and *b,* and as compared with an ordinary transport (1) in *c.*

Right, a DeHavilland Otter. This light STOL transport is popular for civilian passenger applications.

SHORT TAKEOFF AND
LANDING (STOL)

a)

Obstacle — 50 ft

Runway
1,500 ft

Obstacle — 50 ft

b)

Obstacle — 50 ft

Runway
1,500 ft

2

1

c)   Runway

3°

Aircraft Carrier

In 1910, a mere 7 years after the Wright Brothers became airborne over the beaches of North Carolina, a fellow American named Eugene Ely began launching airplanes from the decks of cruising ships, landing on decks embanked with sandbags to prevent the plane from hitting the water. The first aircraft carrier was converted from a merchant-class British ship in 1918. Named the H.M.S. *Argus,* it had an unobstructed flight deck about 560 feet (170 m) long and 64 feet (20 m) wide. During World War I, British seaplanes that were used for scouting enemy ships and planes took off from the water, having been lowered into the sea from the carrier by cranes. Landings were dangerous on such a small and moving ship, but they were performed with reasonably good results most of the time.

the U.S. Pacific fleet (except for its own carriers, which later played the key role in the Coral Sea and Midway battles).

Carriers built after World War II were redesigned to accommodate jet aircraft. The American *Forrestal* class carriers, built between 1952 and 1959, had a flight deck and island that angled at 8 degrees and sponsoned (hung out over the water) out to twice the width of the hull. Four steam catapults launched aircraft at a rate of one every 30 seconds, and much of the ship's operating machinery was automated.

Nuclear-Powered Carriers

The next major advance in carrier construction was the introduction of nuclear-powered ships in 1960. The U.S.S. *Enterprise* has eight nuclear reactors that en-

of the incoming planes. As the aircraft passes over the flight deck, its engines operate at 95-percent capacity. To land, the plane must lower a tail hook and catch one of four steel arrestor cables strung across the flight deck of the carrier so that it comes to a full stop in 200 to 300 feet (60-90 m).

Because the *Enterprise* is nuclear-powered, it differs markedly from its predecessors. Earlier oil-fueled ships required the presence of smokestacks and boiler air intakes on the flight deck. The *Enterprise* eliminates the need for these fragile extrusions that clutter the area near the control tower. *Enterprise*'s streamlined island is topped with a squared-off dome flanked with "billboards" (radar antennas). At the time of their construction, *Enterprise*-class carriers were the largest warships ever

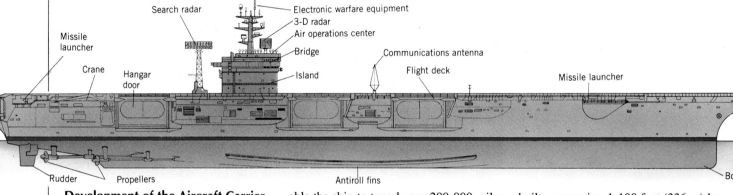

Search radar — Electronic warfare equipment — 3-D radar — Air operations center — Bridge — Missile launcher — Crane — Hangar door — Island — Communications antenna — Flight deck — Missile launcher — Rudder — Propellers — Antiroll fins — Bo

Development of the Aircraft Carrier

In 1922, the U.S. Navy coal-ship *Jupiter* was converted to carry aircraft and renamed the U.S.S. *Langley.* Its top deck was razed and replaced with a wooden flight deck. Airplanes were hoisted from the ship's holds by mechanical cranes. Seaplanes also could be retrieved from the ocean by cranes alongside the ship. That same year, the Japanese built the first carrier, the *Hosho,* from the hull up. In the same period, the British also began to experiment further with carriers. After a few trial runs, they realized that a control tower was needed on the flight deck to coordinate flight operations. A superstructure called an island was located amidships, on the starboard side of the vessel. The Royal Navy also angled the flight deck to prevent collisions during takeoffs and landings, and built steam-driven catapults to boost takeoffs.

Carriers proved so effective a development in naval warfare that the May 1942 Battle of the Coral Sea was the first sea battle during which no shots were fired between any ships. The Japanese bombing of America's Pearl Harbor naval base only months before in December 1941 had already proven that the aircraft carrier was a navy's most important ship. Six carriers carried the planes that crippled most of

able the ship to travel over 200,000 miles (322,000 km) in 3 years without refueling. Its flight deck covers 4.5 acres (1.75 ha) and rises 123 feet (37 m) above the sea's surface. The hangar deck, where the aircraft are stored, is linked to the flight deck by four deck-edge aircraft elevators. Four catapults hurl planes into the air from a gallery deck located directly beneath the flight deck. For takeoff, an airplane taxis into position at the end of a catapult, and a launch bridle is attached to one end of the plane. As its jet engines roar, hot gases that stream from the engines hit water-cooled blast deflectors rising from the deck behind the catapults. This huge moving launch platform suddenly propels the aircraft 20 to 30 feet (6-9 m) into the air, and the aircraft engines accelerate so fast that the plane goes from 0 to 160 miles (260 m) an hour within one minute.

When one of the 95 *Enterprise*-based airplanes wishes to return to the ship, it must circle the carrier in a holding pattern, much as commercial aircraft do at land-based airports. The naval aircraft circles the ship in a counterclockwise direction, until guided by a "meatball" (a pennant) into a landing pattern. The landing signal officer receives instructions for the landing from television monitors equipped with radar that measure the speed

built, measuring 1,100 feet (336 m) long, able to carry 3,100 officers and enlisted men and 2,400 flight personnel, as well as up to 90 airplanes and helicopters.

The Newest Aircraft Carriers

The first nuclear-powered *Nimitz*-class American carrier was launched in 1972. The *Nimitz* is powered by two nuclear reactors, as opposed to the *Enterprise*'s eight, that enable it to travel for up to 13 years without refueling—the improved nuclear engines generate the energy equivalent of 11 million barrels of fuel oil. The space saved within the ship is filled with ordnance, spare parts, and life-support supplies.

Each *Nimitz*-class carrier maintains an aviation group of up to 95 aircraft, including Hawkeye early-warning-system planes, large Tomcat jet fighters that can engage up to six enemy air targets at one time with 60-mile (90-km)-range air-to-air missiles, and a number of long-range A-6 and A-7 jet-strike aircraft. A crew of about 6,100 sailors is needed to operate this ship and its aircraft.

Although they are very powerful and threatening to behold, the future of aircraft carriers appears uncertain. The *Nimitz*-class construction cost is over $2,000 million, a figure that has seemed increas-

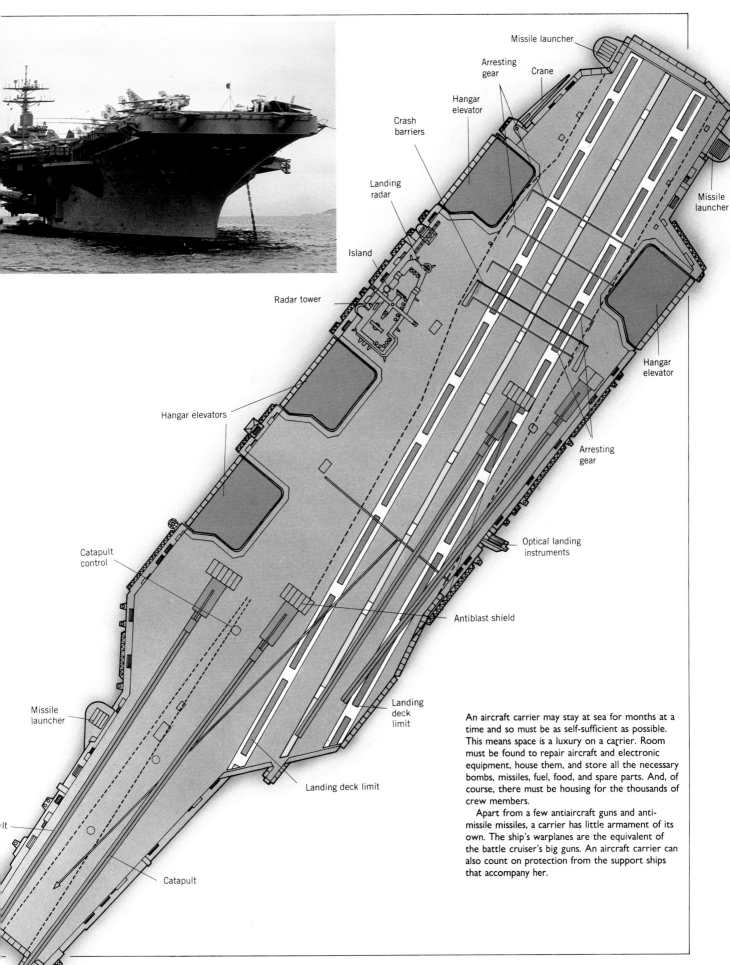

Missile launcher

Arresting gear

Crane

Hangar elevator

Crash barriers

Landing radar

Island

Radar tower

Missile launcher

Hangar elevators

Arresting gear

Optical landing instruments

Catapult control

Antiblast shield

Missile launcher

Landing deck limit

Landing deck limit

Catapult

lt

An aircraft carrier may stay at sea for months at a time and so must be as self-sufficient as possible. This means space is a luxury on a carrier. Room must be found to repair aircraft and electronic equipment, house them, and store all the necessary bombs, missiles, fuel, food, and spare parts. And, of course, there must be housing for the thousands of crew members.

Apart from a few antiaircraft guns and anti-missile missiles, a carrier has little armament of its own. The ship's warplanes are the equivalent of the battle cruiser's big guns. An aircraft carrier can also count on protection from the support ships that accompany her.

ingly exorbitant to some critics. The United States launched its third *Nimitz*-class carrier in 1981, the *Carl Vinson*, which may well be the last warship of its size or launching capability, except for the huge Soviet nuclear carrier underway in 1983. One aircraft that may lessen the need for such costly behemoths is the British Sea Harrier jet fighter. This plane weighs one-third of the Tomcat and can take off from a vertical position, land on a much smaller airstrip than any other plane now in use, and land at sea without the traditional arresting gear for stopping. The Harrier can also be launched from smaller warships like destroyers or frigates. The British *Invincible*-class carrier has been developed with a new kind of runway, a "ski-jump," to accommodate these jets. Adapting existing carriers to Harrier proportions costs about a quarter of the amount needed to build the *Invincible* ships.

Modern aircraft carriers have two runways; one, shorter, for catapult-assisted takeoffs, and another, longer one for landings. A series of arresting cables helps bring landing aircraft to a halt within available space.

Antiblast shield

Jet awaiting takeoff

Special instrumentation helps pilots in the difficult task of landing on a moving carrier deck. Both optical and microwave systems help guide pilots to the correct landing approach angle.

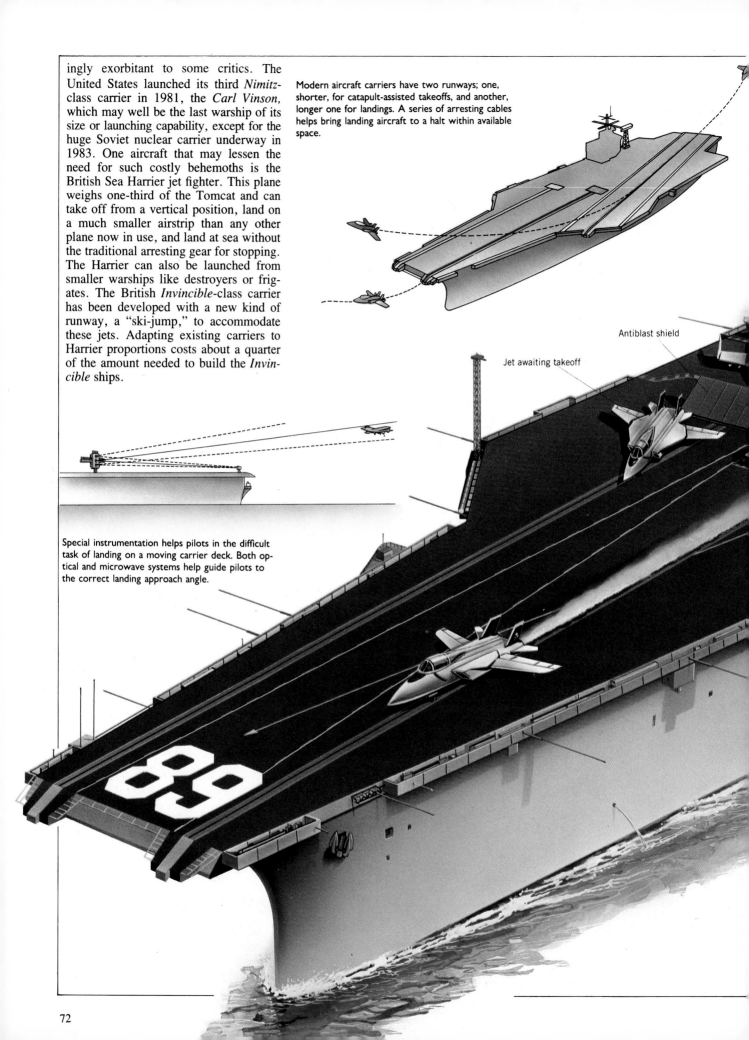

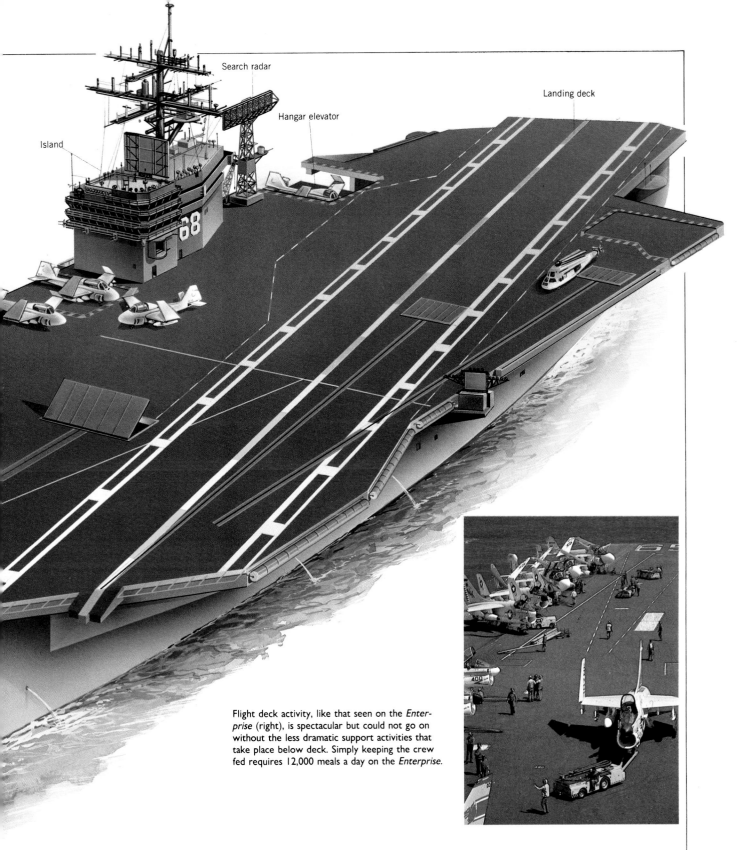

Island

Search radar

Hangar elevator

Landing deck

68

Flight deck activity, like that seen on the *Enterprise* (right), is spectacular but could not go on without the less dramatic support activities that take place below deck. Simply keeping the crew fed requires 12,000 meals a day on the *Enterprise*.

Despite the vast size and weight of the modern aircraft carrier (the *Nimitz*-class ships each displace over 90,000 tons of water with a full load), they are the fastest surface warships ever built, capable of moving at speeds of up to 33 knots. Since they carry few defensive weapons on board, carriers usually travel in task-force groups comprised of well-armed destroyers, submarines, and cruise-missile ships. The sight of one of these naval groups, with a flat-topped, bottle-shaped airport at its center, often has prevented potential conflict at sea during the last 40-odd years.

Airplane

The airplane is a machine of the ultimate. When Wilbur and Orville Wright were testing their first Flyer in the dunes of Kitty Hawk in North Carolina in 1903, they were going for broke. They would either fly or they wouldn't; if they flew, they would either learn at once how to fly safely, or they would crash. The airplane knows no middle ground.

To justify such risks, the rewards must be great. The airplane is a tool of transportation, and seldom in the long history of transportation has anything held such potential. The airplane promised speed. It promised convenience. It promised access to distant places. It promised to cancel out mountains, deserts, oceans. But few would have believed, on that windy December morning in 1903, that the airplane also promised other worlds.

Man's dream had always been to fly like a bird, to soar effortlessly on the wind like an eagle. But airplanes with flapping wings—known as ornithopters—never worked. No man-made machine could match the power of the pectoral muscles of a bird. The reality, when it came, was quite different.

It came with the power of the wind flowing over the curved surface of a wing. Above the upper surface of the wing, a relative vacuum was formed by the speed of the wind; this was the lifting force. But to create this force, to create the wind that brought it into being, the airplane had to move forward.

Flight in the Open

The first practical airplanes, small and light, flew at such slow speeds that pilot and passengers—if there were any—sat out in the open, most often on the wing. There was little practical use for these early types. But, in 1911, a Wright biplane completed the first flight across the American continent—a flight marked by frequent forced landings and delays, but that took its pilot, Calvin Galbraith Rodgers, from ocean to ocean and proved that the potential of the airplane was not a dream.

World War I brought the pressure that the airplane needed to be sent firmly on its way. Planes entered the war unarmed, cruising above the battlefield to observe enemy troop movements, correct artillery fire, and map trenches and emplacements. Soon, however, pilots began to fire pistols at each other and to drop grenades on troops below. Then they mounted machine guns, and devices were invented to prevent the bullets from hitting the spinning propeller blades. Speed increased; pushed by tactics of survival, the single-seat fighter planes became nimble birds of death, and a full-scale war in the air was on.

Bank to left   Bank to right

The great variety of flying animals and flying machines shows that there is more than one solution to the problem of flight.

Whatever the answer, though, three essential difficulties must be overcome. The first is the power source. In birds this is the wing muscle; in airplanes, the engine. The other two problems, stability in flight and maneuverability, are met in a similar way by both birds and aircraft. Both depend on changing the shape of wing and tail surfaces.

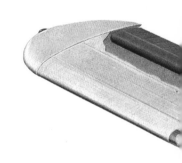

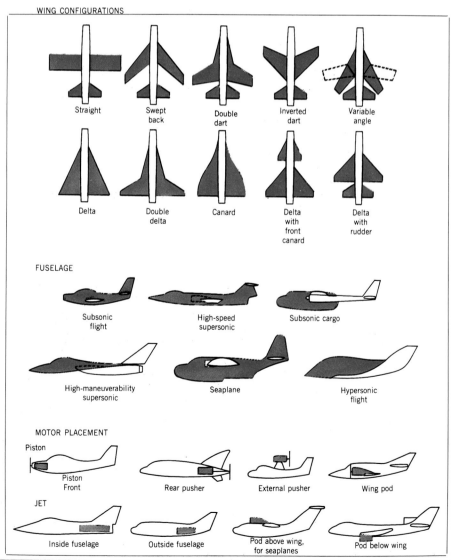

WING CONFIGURATIONS

Straight — Swept back — Double dart — Inverted dart — Variable angle

Delta — Double delta — Canard — Delta with front canard — Delta with rudder

FUSELAGE

Subsonic flight — High-speed supersonic — Subsonic cargo

High-maneuverability supersonic — Seaplane — Hypersonic flight

MOTOR PLACEMENT

Piston

Piston Front — Rear pusher — External pusher — Wing pod

JET

Inside fuselage — Outside fuselage — Pod above wing, for seaplanes — Pod below wing

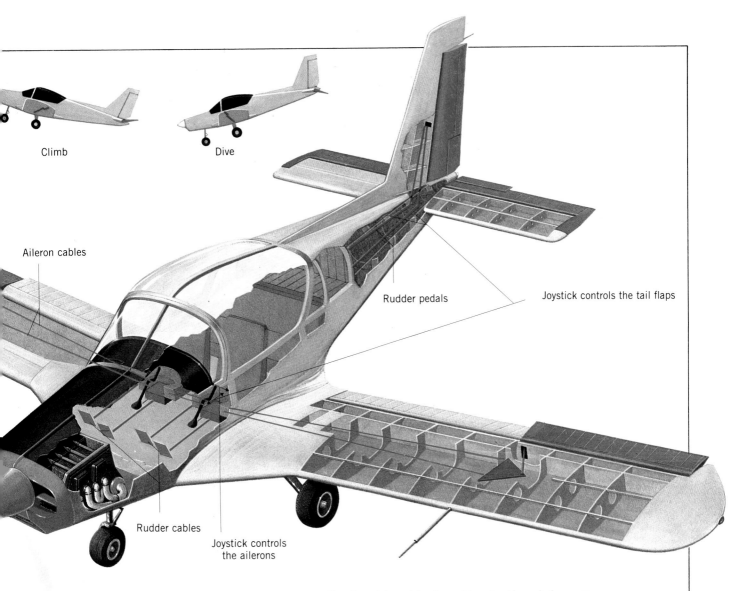

Climb

Dive

Aileron cables

Rudder pedals

Joystick controls the tail flaps

Rudder cables

Joystick controls
the ailerons

Left: The table indicates some of the many possible wing, fuselage, and engine configurations used to design aircraft with different flight and speed characteristics.

Top: From left to right, the position of rudder and aileron control surfaces during the four basic aircraft maneuvers; left bank, right bank, climb, and dive.
The large cutaway design shows how these control surfaces are governed by the rudder pedals and joystick in the cockpit.

Size increased as well. Behind combat lines, in the homelands of the warring nations, industries and cities were within reach of airplanes carrying bombs. Multi-engined, with crews of as many as seven men, the big bombers flew by night to drop their high explosives, foreshadowing terrible wars of destruction still to come.

After World War I, civil aviation was born in the skies of Europe, which so lately had echoed to the chattering of machine guns and the thud of bombs. The German *Lufthansa* airline—the world's first—was launched in 1919. Great Britain and France soon followed. America lagged far behind. Barnstorming and flying circuses were all the American public was interested insofar as the airplane was concerned, and it would be nearly a dozen years before serious efforts to promote travel by air would be made.

By the 1920s, the airplane had progressed far enough in design and construction to be taken seriously as a new means of transportation, and in Europe it was. European passengers were no longer offered converted bombers to ride in. Cabins were luxurious and comfortable, with cushions on the seats, pictures on the walls, and food and drink on the table. Often, pilot and crew were still out in the breeze, but those conditions would not prevail much longer.

Engines still left much to be desired in reliability, and any flight might be interrupted by a forced landing. But in the slow, low-flying planes of the day (London to Paris took 2½ hours), this was generally no more than an inconvenience. There were plenty of open fields to land on, and the mechanic on board could make repairs quickly. Navigation was a primi-

tive matter of following roads and railroads, and some pilots even found ways of getting where they wanted to go in fog. Gordon Olley, for example, a British pilot, took to following the lines of turbulence left by express trains plowing through the murk.

Routes to the Empire

The range of the commercial airliner of the 1920s generally did not exceed 300 to 400 miles (500-650 km), which meant careful planning of refueling stops en route. Nonetheless, with the help of government subsidies, airline routes continued to expand. By the middle of the decade, Great Britain had established Imperial Airways, formed by consolidating all existing airlines into one government-run line, and was pioneering routes that

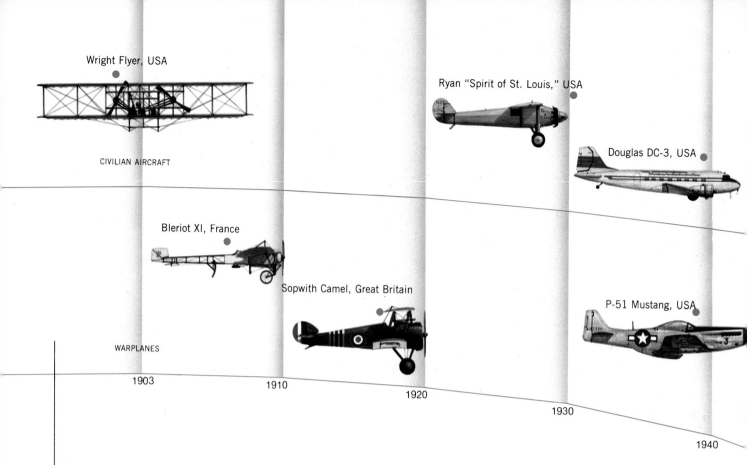

Wright Flyer, USA

Ryan "Spirit of St. Louis," USA

Douglas DC-3, USA

CIVILIAN AIRCRAFT

Bleriot XI, France

Sopwith Camel, Great Britain

P-51 Mustang, USA

WARPLANES

1903   1910   1920   1930   1940

linked all corners of the then far-flung British empire.

With 14 to 15 passengers per plane, airline operation was a losing proposition for most of the 1920s, and technology was slow in improving matters. Right up through the early thirties the typical airliner was a large, boxy affair, with two engines on the biplane wings and perhaps a third in the nose. But then, in the United States, a new silhouette appeared: slim, streamlined, with wheels that folded up into the wings and wings that were free of any kind of speed-robbing struts or wires. The Douglas DC-3 typified the new type of airliner, and it bore out the promise of its appearance by flying from New York to Los Angeles in 24 hours, including intermediate stops. For the first time in America, the airplane was faster than the railroad train, and over the vast distances of North America, that made the difference. Air travel, hitherto the stepchild of the transportation industry in the United States, began to pick up in popularity.

Flying Boats: A Short, Romantic Life

An important factor in the growth of air transport around the world was the flying boat, a roomy plane built to cross the oceans with unprecedented luxury and safety. It had some impressive forebears: the pioneering German Dornier Wal flying boats of the 1920s, which had helped to pave the airways to South America, and the huge, 12-engined Dornier DoX, which

was equipped for 174 passengers and flew to New York in 1930.

In Britain, Short-Sunderland and Saunders-Roe were both building large flying boats for Imperial Airways, and for a while it seemed that this type of aircraft, with its large carrying capacity and its comforting ability to survive on water, would be the answer to intercontinental flight. In the United States, Sikorski, Martin, and Boeing were the leading manufacturers of this type of aircraft, and by 1939, two of them had ocean-spanning airliners. The Boeing 314 Clipper could carry up to 89 passengers and had a range of 5,200 miles (8,300 km), enough for nonstop Pacific crossings. The Sikorski flying boats dominated the South American traffic, opening new routes for Pan-American Airways, which emerged as the leading world airline of the time. But World War II effectively ended commercial flying boat development, and by the time it was over, land-based planes had built up an insurmountable lead in range and reliability.

In the 1930s, two technological developments played a major role in advancing the airplane as a transportation tool: the retractable landing gear and the variable-pitch propeller. Removing the heavy wheels and struts from the slipstream and fairing them into the wings and fuselage significantly increased an airplane's cruising speed and range. The variable-pitch propeller was to the airplane what a gear

shift is to a car; it provided different gear ratios for different jobs. One added power for takeoffs, thus permitting heavier loads and shorter takeoff runs. Another provided power for climbing, while at the same time improving the rate of climb. And a third, for cruising at high altitude, increased both speed and range—two factos that differentiate a money-making airline from a money-losing one.

Jets: A Quantum Leap

In the postwar era, the decisive technological development was the jet engine. This extraordinary power plant, so totally unlike the piston engines that had served the airplane from the Wright brothers' first flight, moved commercial flight a quantum leap forward. Speeds more than doubled. Range increased to the point where transoceanic flights with no refueling stops became routine. Altitude mounted upward to the thin, clear air of 50,000 feet (15,000 m) above sea level. The power of the jet engine was phenomenal; passenger loads jumped to 100, then 200 passengers, and more.

These postwar developments phased the flying boats out of the aviation picture for good, yet they did not die easily. Their roominess and the safety factor of being able to land on water were still prized, but their speed limitations were absolute, and relative to their size, their carrying capacity could not compete with that of land planes. A few efforts were made to adapt

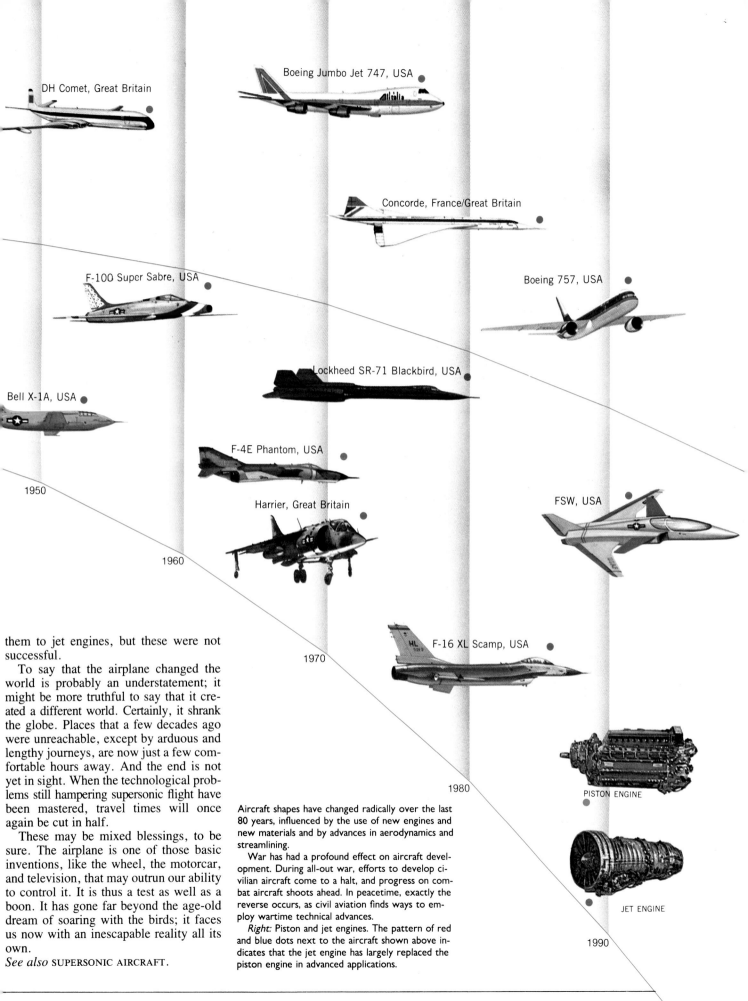

DH Comet, Great Britain

Boeing Jumbo Jet 747, USA

Concorde, France/Great Britain

F-100 Super Sabre, USA

Boeing 757, USA

Lockheed SR-71 Blackbird, USA

Bell X-1A, USA

F-4E Phantom, USA

1950

FSW, USA

Harrier, Great Britain

1960

F-16 XL Scamp, USA

1970

1980

PISTON ENGINE

JET ENGINE

1990

them to jet engines, but these were not successful.

To say that the airplane changed the world is probably an understatement; it might be more truthful to say that it created a different world. Certainly, it shrank the globe. Places that a few decades ago were unreachable, except by arduous and lengthy journeys, are now just a few comfortable hours away. And the end is not yet in sight. When the technological problems still hampering supersonic flight have been mastered, travel times will once again be cut in half.

These may be mixed blessings, to be sure. The airplane is one of those basic inventions, like the wheel, the motorcar, and television, that may outrun our ability to control it. It is thus a test as well as a boon. It has gone far beyond the age-old dream of soaring with the birds; it faces us now with an inescapable reality all its own.

See also SUPERSONIC AIRCRAFT.

Aircraft shapes have changed radically over the last 80 years, influenced by the use of new engines and new materials and by advances in aerodynamics and streamlining.

War has had a profound effect on aircraft development. During all-out war, efforts to develop civilian aircraft come to a halt, and progress on combat aircraft shoots ahead. In peacetime, exactly the reverse occurs, as civil aviation finds ways to employ wartime technical advances.

Right: Piston and jet engines. The pattern of red and blue dots next to the aircraft shown above indicates that the jet engine has largely replaced the piston engine in advanced applications.

Airplane Design

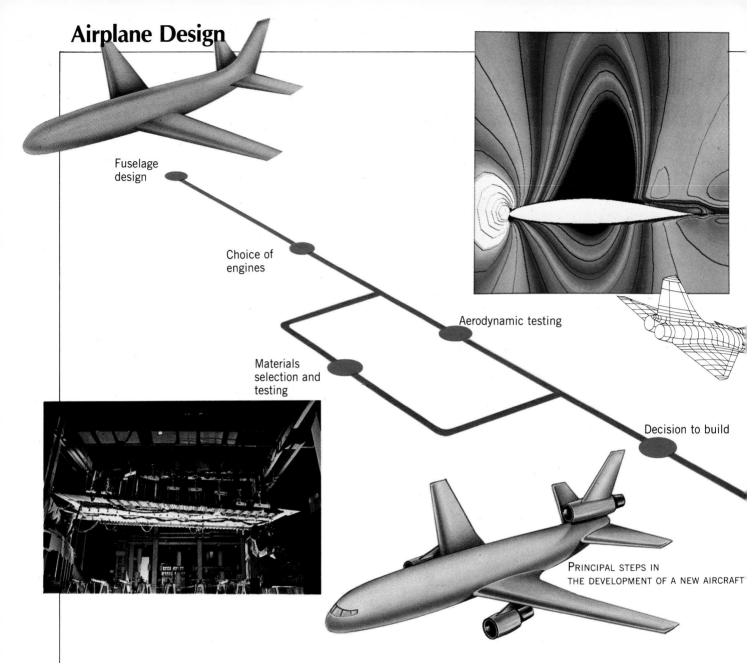

Fuselage design

Choice of engines

Aerodynamic testing

Materials selection and testing

Decision to build

PRINCIPAL STEPS IN
THE DEVELOPMENT OF A NEW AIRCRAFT

How to design an airplane? Scarcely a hundred years ago, there were probably not half a dozen persons in the world who could answer that question, for in the closing years of the 19th century there existed not even a fragment of knowledge to tell the would-be builders of airplanes the direction in which they should go.

There were only the birds, sailing, soaring, tantalizingly beyond reach, the secret of flight locked in their graceful wings. And so men who were interested in flying watched them, trying to guess at the mystery.

Wilbur and Orville Wright, two bicycle mechanics from Dayton, Ohio, in 1899 began their systematic scrutiny of everything that might give them a clue about how the birds did it. Nothing in the scientific literature was useful to them; there was no literature on the subject that could be called scientific. But there was for a starting point the work of a German named

Otto Lilienthal, an engineer who had been experimenting with gliders and had kept meticulous notes on his many flights from a hilltop near Berlin. Since Lilienthal had been a close observer of bird flight, it is little wonder that his gliders resembled birds. But he early avoided the pitfall that had lured others, including Leonardo da Vinci: the flapping wing that is the basis of bird flight. Lilienthal demonstrated that a successful aircraft must have a rigid wing that interacts with the air. Only such a wing, he reasoned, could be controlled to the degree necessary to achieve stable flight, and in this the Wrights agreed with him.

Self-made Scientists

Wilbur and Orville Wright were not scientifically educated men; neither of them had gone beyond high school. But as they progressed in their studies of flight, they made scientists of themselves, even to the point of building a body of litera-

ture that was scientific, bolstered as it was by hundreds of experiments with scale models, kites, and man-carrying gliders. They even built a wind tunnel to test the more than 200 different types of wings they designed. When the first Wright Flyer took to the air on December 17, 1903, with Orville at the controls, it was solidly based on sound aerodynamic theory.

Otto Lilienthal and the Wright brothers built the foundations of airplane design. Everything that followed was a refinement of their doctrine of the rigid wing that created lift by its own passage through the air. But the wing itself was not controllable. The Wrights knew that a successful airplane design must incorporate a mechanism that would make the wing stable by allowing the pilot to correct for the upsetting effects of wind gusts and the up- or down-drafts of rough air.

They observed the birds, and noted how they twisted the tips of their wings in

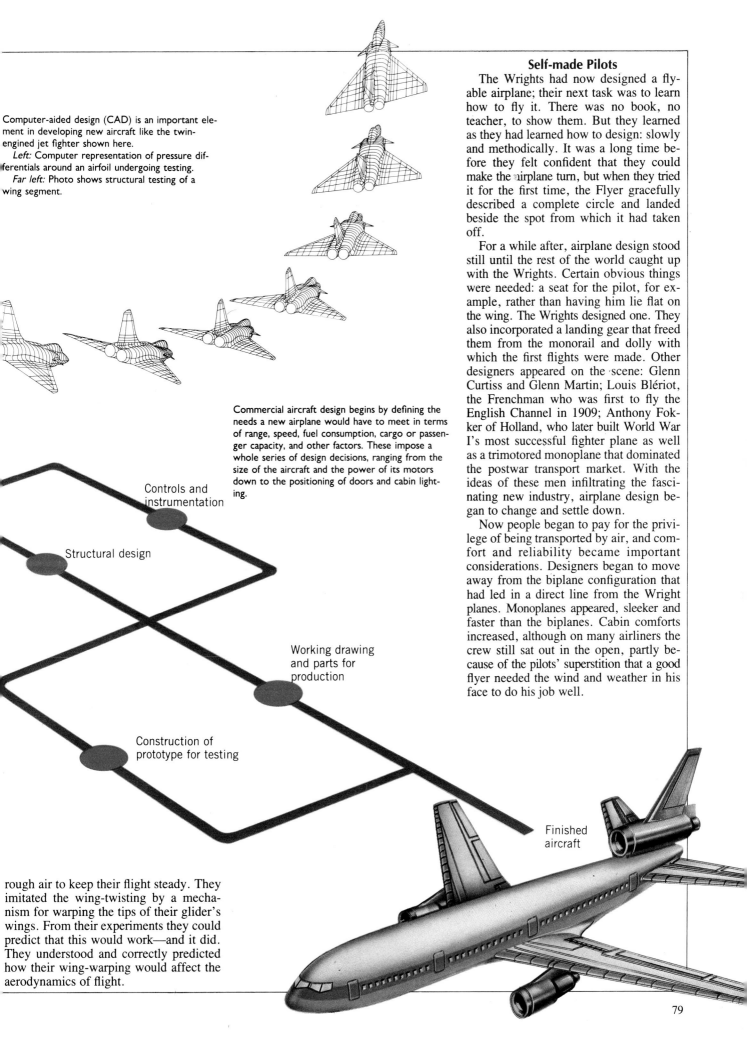

Computer-aided design (CAD) is an important element in developing new aircraft like the twin-engined jet fighter shown here.
Left: Computer representation of pressure differentials around an airfoil undergoing testing.
Far left: Photo shows structural testing of a wing segment.

Commercial aircraft design begins by defining the needs a new airplane would have to meet in terms of range, speed, fuel consumption, cargo or passenger capacity, and other factors. These impose a whole series of design decisions, ranging from the size of the aircraft and the power of its motors down to the positioning of doors and cabin lighting.

Controls and instrumentation

Structural design

Working drawing and parts for production

Construction of prototype for testing

Finished aircraft

Self-made Pilots

The Wrights had now designed a fly-able airplane; their next task was to learn how to fly it. There was no book, no teacher, to show them. But they learned as they had learned how to design: slowly and methodically. It was a long time before they felt confident that they could make the airplane turn, but when they tried it for the first time, the Flyer gracefully described a complete circle and landed beside the spot from which it had taken off.

For a while after, airplane design stood still until the rest of the world caught up with the Wrights. Certain obvious things were needed: a seat for the pilot, for example, rather than having him lie flat on the wing. The Wrights designed one. They also incorporated a landing gear that freed them from the monorail and dolly with which the first flights were made. Other designers appeared on the scene: Glenn Curtiss and Glenn Martin; Louis Blériot, the Frenchman who was first to fly the English Channel in 1909; Anthony Fokker of Holland, who later built World War I's most successful fighter plane as well as a trimotored monoplane that dominated the postwar transport market. With the ideas of these men infiltrating the fascinating new industry, airplane design began to change and settle down.

Now people began to pay for the privilege of being transported by air, and comfort and reliability became important considerations. Designers began to move away from the biplane configuration that had led in a direct line from the Wright planes. Monoplanes appeared, sleeker and faster than the biplanes. Cabin comforts increased, although on many airliners the crew still sat out in the open, partly because of the pilots' superstition that a good flyer needed the wind and weather in his face to do his job well.

rough air to keep their flight steady. They imitated the wing-twisting by a mechanism for warping the tips of their glider's wings. From their experiments they could predict that this would work—and it did. They understood and correctly predicted how their wing-warping would affect the aerodynamics of flight.

Milestones in Design

The turning point of airplane design came in the early 1930s, when the United States, lagging far behind Europe, finally jumped into the air passenger and mail business with both feet. It was clear that the industry could no longer make do with converted military planes; something specifically designed for passenger service was needed. One of the big carriers, United Airlines, approached the Boeing Airplane Company for such a machine.

The result was an aircraft that was entirely new, its design dominated by the dictates of reliability, economy, and speed. It was built wholly of metal, on the new "stressed skin" principle that made the aluminum-alloy skin a working part of the supporting structure. It was designed to fly from coast to coast in less than 24 hours, carrying 14 passengers in solid comfort. It was smoothly streamlined from nose to tail, with no supporting members such as struts to offer wind resistance. Even the landing gear retracted out of the slipstream, and the wing was supported by a single massive internal spar.

This aircraft, the Boeing 247, was a design milestone but a commercial failure; it was eclipsed by the Douglas DC-3 that followed soon after, but it set the pattern for airliner design from then on.

The next milestone in design came with the advent of the jet engine in the years after World War II. With the vastly increased power it afforded, the jet opened a whole new world of speed range, and economy, since the jet could fly at altitudes up to 50,000 feet where its consumption of fuel was at a minimum. It was design for the jet age that paved the way for supersonic flight, which came in the 1970s; and it contributed greatly to design work for the space age, embodied by the U.S. space shuttle, which made its first flight in 1981.

What makes a good airplane? That depends on what it will be used for, but usefulness is a primary consideration. In passenger airlines, this encompasses speed, range, and load-carrying capacity. Since the load is made up of people, the designer is placed in the interesting situation of putting into the airplane comfortable seats, carpets, windows, washrooms, toilets, kitchens, and a water supply. And all of this must function in a pressurized atmosphere, and of course the pressurizing machinery must be accommodated as well.

In less than a hundred years, airplane design has come all the way from nothing to the space age. There is probably no other profession that can compare with that.

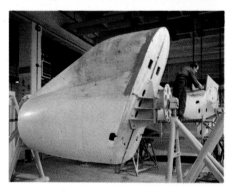

Top: Honeycomb wing structure. *Middle:* Wing panel being machined from a solid slab of super-light metal alloy. *Bottom:* Fiberglass mold over which the body panels covering the nose of an aircraft will be formed.

Right: Construction of prototypes of the Boeing 767 and a stretched version of the 747 'Jumbo Jet.' These prototypes serve as test beds and as samples to show to potential buyers.

Airplane Engine

It is a basic truth in flying that unless an airplane keeps moving it cannot stay in the air. This is because there must be a flow of air over its wings so that lift will be created. In an airplane, the forward motion is provided by a propeller or a jet engine that respectively pulls or pushes the airplane through the air.

The nature of the airplane requires that the engines be in some respects different from those of vehicles operating on the ground. Airplanes operate in three dimensions and must sometimes make sudden and violent maneuvers; they may even have to fly upside down. All the while the engine must continue to function reliably.

The first true aircraft engine was built by the Wright brothers for their own use in powering their first experimental plane, the Wright Flyer. They had been unable to find an engine light enough to suit their purpose, so they finally built one themselves. It is a measure of their skill that they not only succeeded, but that they came up with an engine of 12 horsepower that was still light enough so that their airplane got off the ground on its first try.

The Wrights built a gasoline engine of conventional design, and variations of the gasoline-powered engine continued to dominate the aviation industry for the next 50 years. There were two principal types: in-line engines, in which the cylinders were arranged one behind the other in a straight line, and radial engines, in which the cylinders were clustered in a ring around a central crankshaft. From an aerodynamic viewpoint, the in-line engines were often favored because they could be easily streamlined into a slender aircraft body, while the radial engines, large and blunt with a flat frontal surface, needed elaborate cowlings to fit into a smoothly streamlined design.

The radial engine had one big advantage: it was air-cooled. Like any gasoline engine, an airplane engine gives off large

Aircraft motion is due to the principle of action and reaction. Depending on the power source, an aircraft may produce the desired "reaction" of forward motion by the "action" of forcing air backward with a propeller or forcing exhaust gases backward from a jet engine.

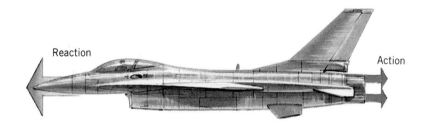

Reaction / Action

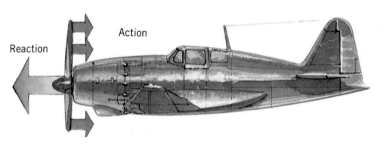

Action / Reaction

amounts of heat while it is running, and this heat must be got rid of somehow. An in-line engine was liquid-cooled, like an auto engine, which added another dimension to its already large area of vulnerability to damage, particularly in military airplanes. A radial engine had unlimited cooling available in the wind of its own passing.

A World War I variant of the radial engine, which is a curiosity today, was the so-called rotary engine, in which the entire cylinder assembly spun around an immovable crankshaft fixed in the center. The propeller was affixed to the bank of cylinders and spun with them. The rotary engine, too, was air-cooled, and though it

functioned well enough to be in general use in the Allied air forces, the twisting forces created by having the entire engine spin around at high speeds were so great that it was finally abandoned.

By the mid-1930s, the radial engine had become the favored engine for the passenger airliner. It had advantages in both lightness and power that the in-line engines could not match. As the airline industry grew and expanded, radial engines grew in size and horsepower until double-banked radials with two rows of cylinders developed 2,000 and more horsepower, and their range of 5,000 miles (8,000 km) made intercontinental flights a reality.

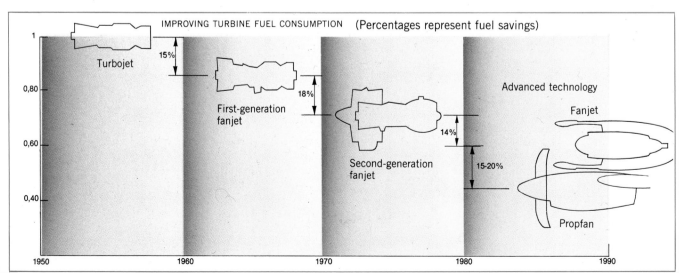

IMPROVING TURBINE FUEL CONSUMPTION (Percentages represent fuel savings)

Turbojet — 15% — First-generation fanjet — 18% — Second-generation fanjet — 14% — 15-20% — Advanced technology — Fanjet — Propfan

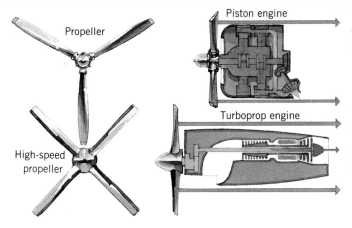

Propeller

High-speed propeller

Piston engine

Turboprop engine

The propeller virtually disappeared from larger aircraft during the 1960's. Effective at low speeds, traditional propellers become very inefficient when blade velocities approach the speed of sound.

Today, though, improved aerodynamic designs like the four-bladed propeller on the right permit speeds up to 500 miles (800 km) per hour as opposed to the 375 miles (600 km) per hour once thought to be their upper limit. These advanced propellers, coupled with turbine engines, offer attactive economy in fuel consumption.

The close of World War II brought the jet engine on the scene, and with it a revolution in aviation. When jets came into common use in the mid-1950s, the world shrank overnight, and the airplane for the first time became a truly common carrier.

The principle of the jet engine is not difficult to grasp. Whereas a propeller-driving engine pushes an airplane forward by gathering up great volumes of air and pushing them backward, a jet engine gathers in huge quantities of air and pushes

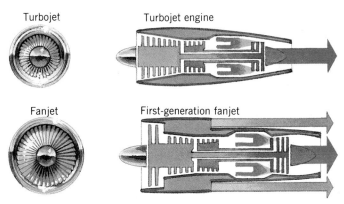

Turbojet

Turbojet engine

Fanjet

First-generation fanjet

The advantages of fanjet engines as opposed to the older turbojet design are greater fuel efficiency and lower noise levels.

The fanjet obtains thrust not only from engine exhaust gases, but also by using the fan, which is really a sophisticated propeller, to drive air out the back of the engine housing.

In the engine designs on the left, the red arrows indicate the flow of exhaust gases; the blue arrows represent air flow.

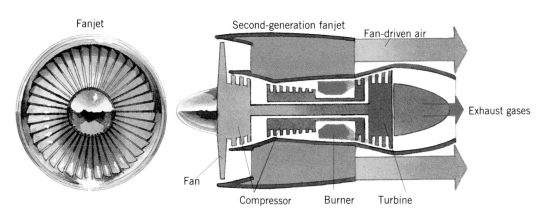

Fanjet

Second-generation fanjet

Fan-driven air

Exhaust gases

Fan

Compressor   Burner   Turbine

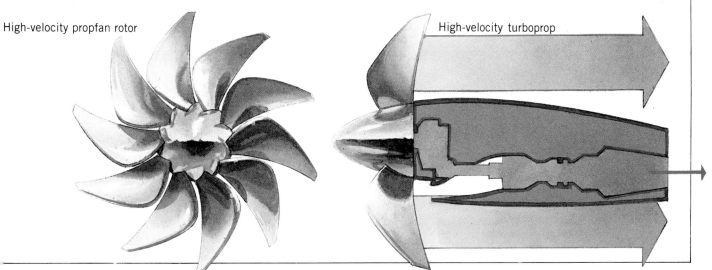

High-velocity propfan rotor

High-velocity turboprop

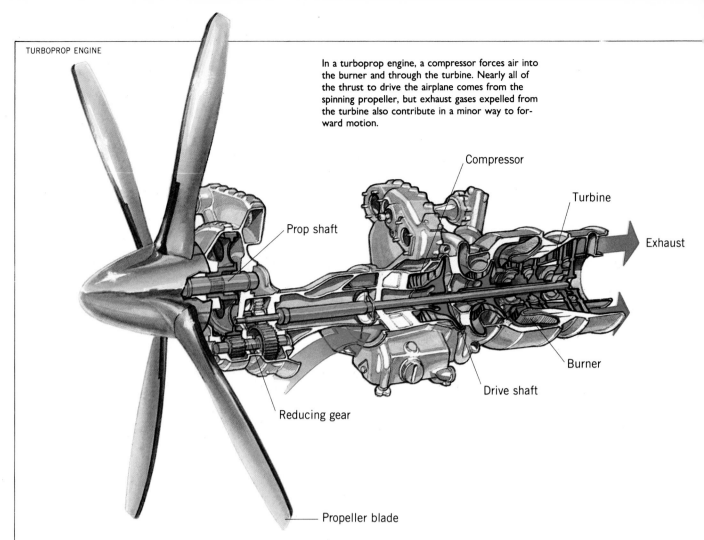

In a turboprop engine, a compressor forces air into the burner and through the turbine. Nearly all of the thrust to drive the airplane comes from the spinning propeller, but exhaust gases expelled from the turbine also contribute in a minor way to forward motion.

Compressor

Turbine

Exhaust

Prop shaft

Burner

Drive shaft

Reducing gear

Propeller blade

them backward through a compression chamber, using that air to burn, at extremely high temperatures, a fuel-air mixture, which is then ejected backward through an exhaust nozzle. Thus, a jet engine basically uses the surrounding air only as an oxidizing medium, which sustains the intense internal combustion and results in extremely high thrust.

The first large-scale adaptation of the jet engine to commercial use was the so-called turboprop. In this version, the spinning turbine that compressed air for the burning process was geared to a conventional airplane propeller. Versatile and powerful, the turboprop was not as fast as the pure jet engine, but it proved to be extremely adaptable to a wide range of uses. It is still in service today, particularly on helicopters.

Within a short period, the pure jet engine, more properly known as the turbojet, became the standard engine for passenger transportation by the world's airlines. At cruising altitudes of 30,000 feet (9,000 m) or more, it proved to be efficient in its use of fuel, giving airplanes easy intercontinental range. Cruising speeds of 550 mph (900 kph) became routine, cutting the flight time across the Atlantic Ocean in half. Direct, nonstop

service to distant places could be initiated, and no part of the world was beyond reach.

As of this writing, space travel is also in an advanced experimental stage, with the space shuttle a reality. This brings into play still another type of aircraft engine: the rocket. Having proved its reliability on manned flights to the Moon and deep space probes to far distant planets, the

rocket engine is already in guarded use on military aircraft. Whether it will be adapted to commercial use is impossible to say; so far, the need for it has not yet been felt. Meanwhile, its development on the space shuttle brings it close enough to make it a viable candidate for civilian use when the need does arise.

See also AERODYNAMICS; AND AERONAUTICS; ENGINE, INTERNAL COMBUSTION.

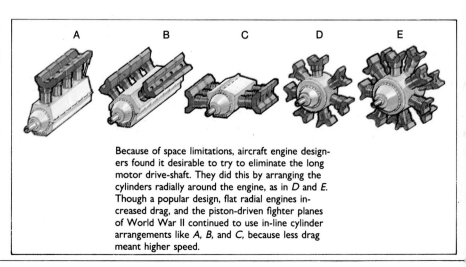

Because of space limitations, aircraft engine designers found it desirable to try to eliminate the long motor drive-shaft. They did this by arranging the cylinders radially around the engine, as in *D* and *E*. Though a popular design, flat radial engines increased drag, and the piston-driven fighter planes of World War II continued to use in-line cylinder arrangements like *A*, *B*, and *C*, because less drag meant higher speed.

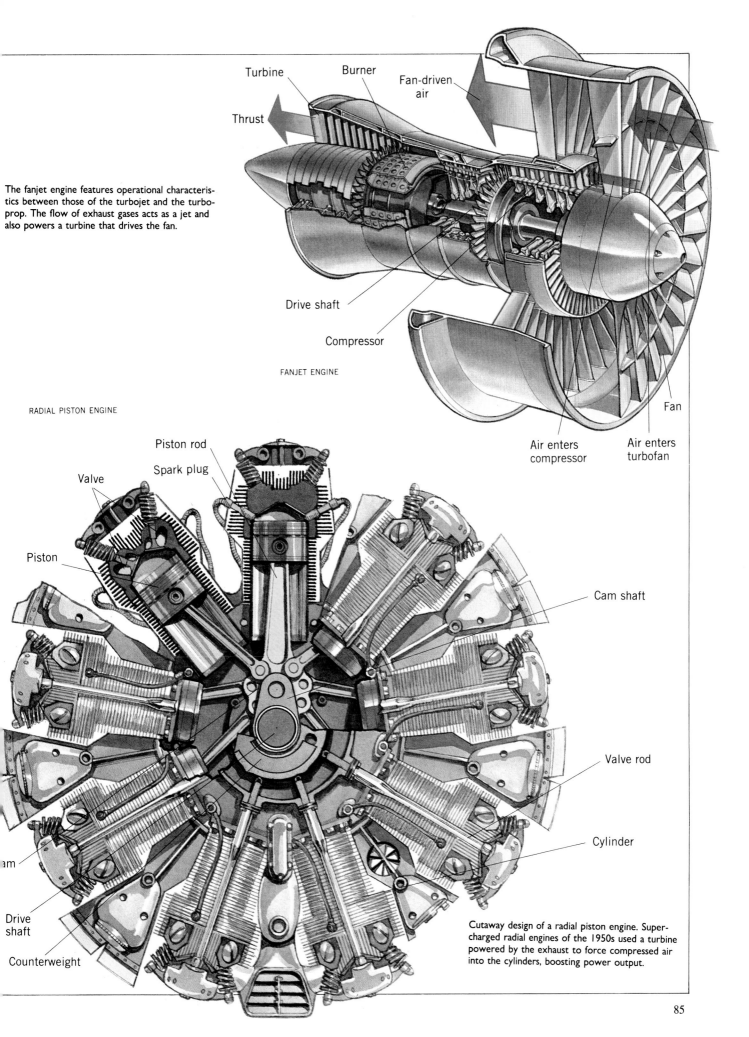

Turbine

Burner

Fan-driven
air

Thrust

The fanjet engine features operational characteristics between those of the turbojet and the turboprop. The flow of exhaust gases acts as a jet and
also powers a turbine that drives the fan.

Drive shaft

Compressor

FANJET ENGINE

Fan

Air enters
compressor

Air enters
turbofan

RADIAL PISTON ENGINE

Piston rod

Spark plug

Valve

Piston

Cam shaft

Valve rod

Cylinder

am

Drive
shaft

Counterweight

Cutaway design of a radial piston engine. Super-
charged radial engines of the 1950s used a turbine
powered by the exhaust to force compressed air
into the cylinders, boosting power output.

85

Airplane Production

In airplanes as in boats, what they do dictates how they are built. Airplanes must fly, and every phase of their design, every detail of their structure, reflects this. Two considerations dominate: lightness and strength.

Compared to an automobile, an airplane is relatively simple to build. Structurally, it can be separated into two basic parts with two different jobs to do. The wings, including tail surfaces, carry the weight of the entire aircraft, and the fuselage carries the cargo, either passengers or freight. These two basic components both need to be light and strong, but of the two, the wings need to be strongest, and they must be flexible as well, in order to accommodate the turbulence they will inevitably encounter in the air.

The first airplanes were built of wood, usually by hand, of Sitka spruce. The wing was built up from a strong spar, which ran its full length and to which were fastened ribs that defined the width and camber, or profile curvature, of the wing. The leading, or front, edge of the wing was where the curvature was most pronounced. It was often sheathed with a thin sheet of wood for protection. The finished wing was then covered with silk or canvas, which was varnished, or "doped," to shrink it and give it surface smoothness.

The earliest aircraft had no fuselage. The pilot sat or lay on the wing, which also carried the engine, and what we now know as the fuselage was simply an open framework extending rearward to support the tail surfaces. Later, this framework was covered over with canvas, and a cockpit was installed to get the pilot in out of the weather. The framework, or fuselage, then also came to accommodate a simple landing gear (two wheels on shock-absorbent struts) and a tail skid.

A Radically New Design

The modern passenger airplane as we know it took on its basic shape in the early 1930s. The airline industry, still in its infancy, was struggling along mostly with war surplus airplanes, and a fast, reliable, comfortable plane to carry passengers was urgently needed. In 1933, Boeing came up with the 247, a radically new design with as many innovations on the inside as on the outside.

The Boeing 247 was a twin-engine monoplane with a retractable landing gear, and even sitting on the ground it looked fast. Its wide, tapered wing had no outside struts to support it. It was built on the cantilever principle, with the full weight of the airplane supported on a single spar that was firmly anchored in the fuselage.

The most novel aspect of the 247, however, was its all-metal construction, which incorporated the new stressed-skin principle. Wood and fabric were gone forever; this airplane gleamed in bright new aluminum alloy, flush-riveted to the wing ribs and airframe. The skin of the airplane itself was an integral part of the load-carrying structure, providing not only lightness and streamlining but also greater strength than had ever been possible.

It was the 247 that introduced these principles to American aviation, but it was another airplane that carried them to the pinnacle of success. The 247, monopolized by United Airlines, for whom it was originally built, could not quite live up to its advance billing in speed, range, and load-carrying ability. A young designer, Donald Douglas, saw his chance and took it. Almost the 247's look-alike as far as outward appearances were concerned, the Douglas DC-1 could carry four more passengers for the same cost. It was followed quickly by the DC-2 and then the DC-3, destined to become the most famous airplane in aviation history. It was the first to introduce coast-to-coast sleeper travel, and when war came it was in such huge demand as a transport that 11,000 were built in the United States alone, and 2,000 more under license in the Soviet Union.

Cleaning Up the Airplane

Perhaps the most important aspect of the stressed-skin design was that it made it possible to give airplanes an aerodynamically "clean" appearance. The only surfaces now exposed to the wind of the plane's passing were functional surfaces, and these—clean, smooth, and polished—offered minimum resistance to the air. Speed climbed to over 200 miles (320 km) per hour, then to over 300 miles (480 km) per hour. By the end of the 1930s, airplanes were flying more than twice as fast as they had in the decade before.

Structural improvements also made it possible for them to fly farther. Fuel tanks could be hidden in the capacious interiors of the new, streamlined, boxlike monocoque wings. Big, four-engined flying boats conquered the oceanic distances of both the Atlantic and the Pacific, inaugurating regular runs to Europe and Asia.

Airplane production was also revolutionized. Wood as a structural material all but disappeared from the aircraft industry, its place taken by light metal alloys. Only a few light planes—such sports planes as the Piper Cub or the Aeronca "Flying Bathtub"—still used wood and canvas. There was one notable exception

Final assembly of B-747 'Jumbo' jets at the Boeing plant in Seattle, Washington.

among military aircraft: the de Havilland Mosquito, an extremely fast British light bomber and reconnaissance plane built of stressed plywood. It was a highly successful aircraft, but as the one holdout against all-metal construction it could not last beyond the war. By the postwar era the all-metal structures reigned supreme.

The jet engine, when it came in the mid-1950s, wrought a revolution in airplane design and structure. For the first time, there was power to burn, power that could lift even the largest airplanes skyward like homing angels, power to reach altitudes hitherto unattainable for normal aircraft, power to accelerate beyond the speed of sound. And the fact of this power inevitably changed the shape as well as the performance of airplanes.

Speed Means Heat

Among the first to change were structural materials. Aluminum and its alloys had been dominant. Now, other metals crept in: magnesium, stainless steel, molybdenum, titanium. Spot-welding began to replace rivets for fastening, making it possible to provide surfaces of mirror smoothness. With the high speeds made possible by jets, temperature was beginning to be a factor to be considered, since at Mach 2 speeds, twice the speed of sound, aluminum alloys begin to soften from the heat generated by aerodynamic drag, and Mach 2 was not unusual for the faster fighter and reconnaissance airplanes.

Construction took some new forms, too. In earlier times, in the 1920s and '30s, some wooden airplanes had been built with monocoque construction: Wings and fuselage were made of thin, bonded sheets of plywood that, once shaped, were stiffened inside with ribs. The same construction method was now applied to metal, which shaped the wings and the long, tapered bodies. In metal, the monocoque structure was even lighter and stronger than in wood—and every pound saved in construction could be converted into a pound of cargo.

The position and shape of the wings were also changed by the advent of the jet. The wings swept backward, giving the airplane the look of an arrowhead in flight. The aircraft's center of gravity also moved toward the rear, so that the wings were no longer in the forward part, as they had traditionally been, but toward the middle and finally toward the rear. The faster the airplane, the more arrowlike it became. Fighters no longer had wings at all in the conventional sense, but delta-shaped, sharply triangular surfaces as smooth and as flat as a knife.

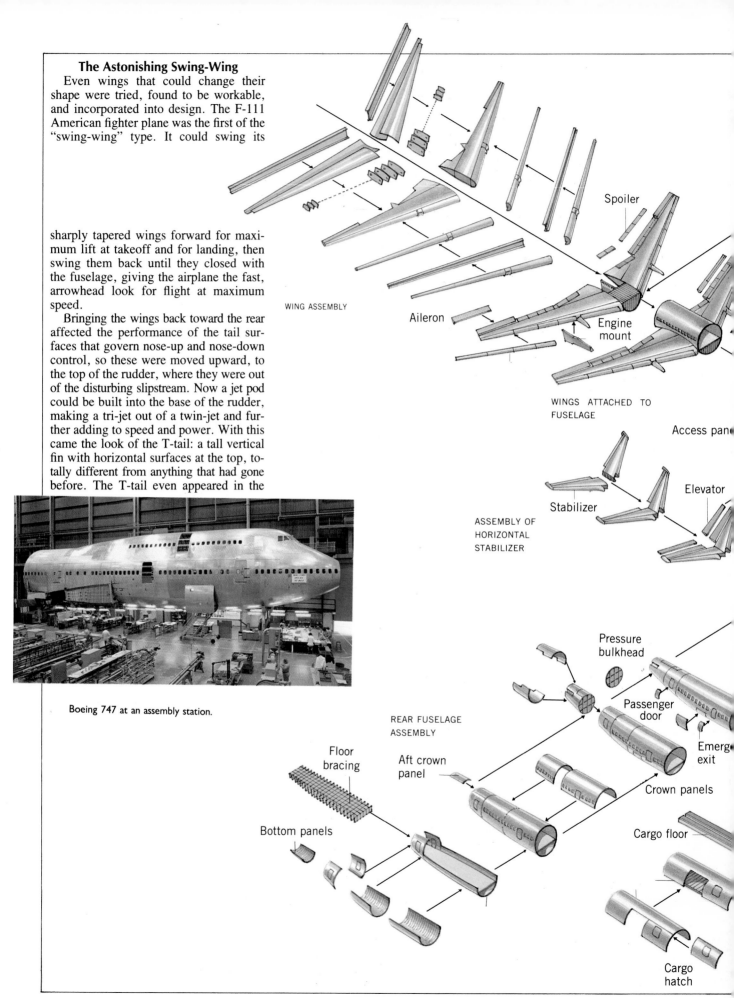

The Astonishing Swing-Wing

Even wings that could change their shape were tried, found to be workable, and incorporated into design. The F-111 American fighter plane was the first of the "swing-wing" type. It could swing its

sharply tapered wings forward for maximum lift at takeoff and for landing, then swing them back until they closed with the fuselage, giving the airplane the fast, arrowhead look for flight at maximum speed.

Bringing the wings back toward the rear affected the performance of the tail surfaces that govern nose-up and nose-down control, so these were moved upward, to the top of the rudder, where they were out of the disturbing slipstream. Now a jet pod could be built into the base of the rudder, making a tri-jet out of a twin-jet and further adding to speed and power. With this came the look of the T-tail: a tall vertical fin with horizontal surfaces at the top, totally different from anything that had gone before. The T-tail even appeared in the

Boeing 747 at an assembly station.

WING ASSEMBLY

Spoiler

Aileron

Engine mount

WINGS ATTACHED TO FUSELAGE

Access pan

Stabilizer

Elevator

ASSEMBLY OF HORIZONTAL STABILIZER

Pressure bulkhead

Passenger door

Emerg exit

Crown panels

REAR FUSELAGE ASSEMBLY

Cargo floor

Floor bracing

Aft crown panel

Bottom panels

Cargo hatch

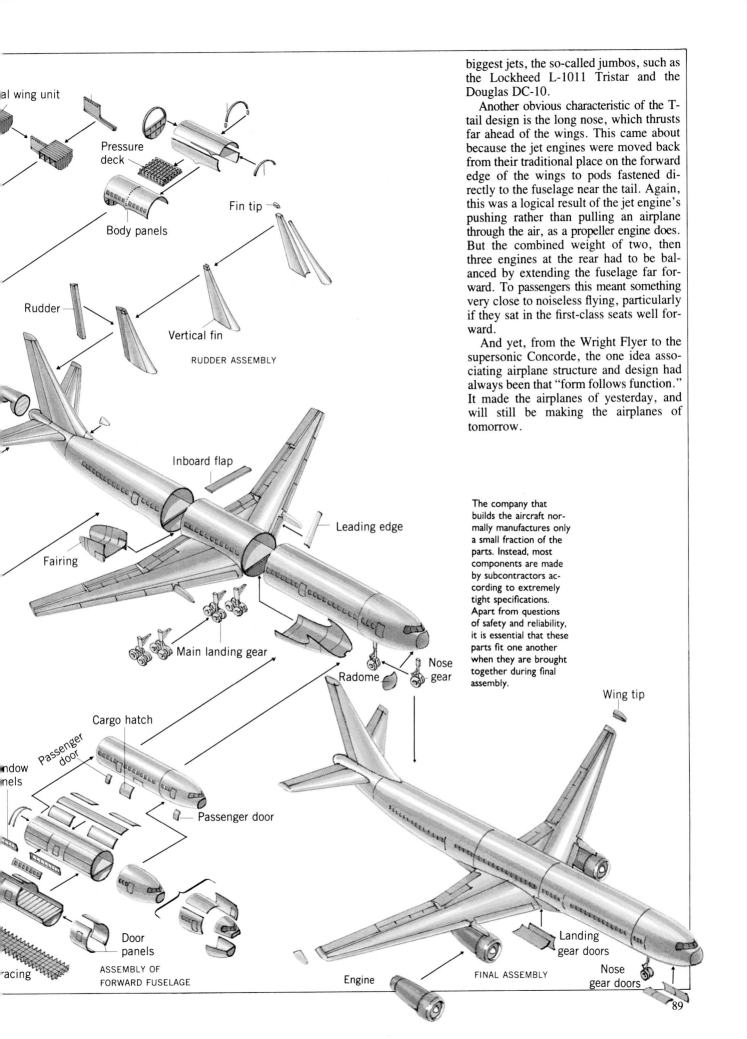

al wing unit

Pressure deck

Body panels

Fin tip

Rudder

Vertical fin

RUDDER ASSEMBLY

Inboard flap

Leading edge

Fairing

Main landing gear

Radome

Nose gear

Wing tip

Cargo hatch

Passenger door

ndow nels

Passenger door

Door panels

acing

ASSEMBLY OF FORWARD FUSELAGE

Engine

FINAL ASSEMBLY

Landing gear doors

Nose gear doors

biggest jets, the so-called jumbos, such as the Lockheed L-1011 Tristar and the Douglas DC-10.

Another obvious characteristic of the T-tail design is the long nose, which thrusts far ahead of the wings. This came about because the jet engines were moved back from their traditional place on the forward edge of the wings to pods fastened directly to the fuselage near the tail. Again, this was a logical result of the jet engine's pushing rather than pulling an airplane through the air, as a propeller engine does. But the combined weight of two, then three engines at the rear had to be balanced by extending the fuselage far forward. To passengers this meant something very close to noiseless flying, particularly if they sat in the first-class seats well forward.

And yet, from the Wright Flyer to the supersonic Concorde, the one idea associating airplane structure and design had always been that "form follows function." It made the airplanes of yesterday, and will still be making the airplanes of tomorrow.

The company that builds the aircraft normally manufactures only a small fraction of the parts. Instead, most components are made by subcontractors according to extremely tight specifications. Apart from questions of safety and reliability, it is essential that these parts fit one another when they are brought together during final assembly.

Airport

In the beginning, there was the open field. Huffman's Prairie, a field in Dayton, Ohio, named for its proprietor, a friend of Wilbur and Orville Wright, was the world's first airport, a place where the Wright brothers perfected their art and their aircraft, circling endlessly in empty skies. They had no traffic worries; theirs was the only airplane flying.

Today, it is not enough to say that airplanes have changed the world; the places where they take off and land—the airports—have undergone some revolutionary changes as well. In 80 years of effort, with our most advanced technology, we have not been able to change the basic attributes of the airplane that make the airport what it has to be: a place of speed and noise and, in this modern age of air traffic, of almost unbelievable congestion.

Airports changed very little for a quarter of a century after the Wright brothers' first flight. They were, in the main, large, flat, open fields of well-packed sod on which airports could land or take off in whatever direction the wind dictated. Usually, there was a small operations shack—where passengers, if there were any, embarked—a gas pump, a hangar or barn for making repairs, and that was all. Charles A. Lindbergh, flying the mails in the 1920s, could describe every hump and hollow in Lambert Field in St. Louis, having had personal experience with all of them.

The New Look

It was in the 1930s, when larger airplanes and more powerful engines made commercial aviation a viable proposition, that airports began to change. They began to evolve along certain very definite lines,

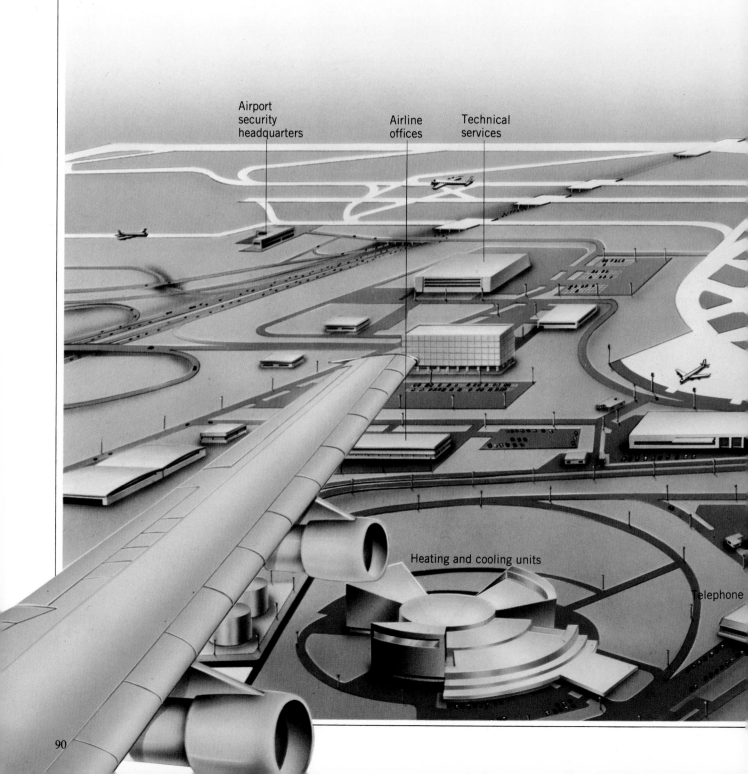

Airport security headquarters

Airline offices

Technical services

Heating and cooling units

Telephone

nd they lost their bucolic look. For the
rst time, runways were paved.

For an airplane to achieve flight, of
ourse, it needs to develop speed and so
nust have a place to gather momentum.
A World-War-I fighter plane, built of
pruce and bamboo and light as a feather,
ould fly in 200 yards (180 m) or less; a
Douglas DC-3 of the mid-1930s, all-
netal, with twin engines and 21 passen-
ers, might need five times that much.
urthermore, for the comfort of passen-
ers and their safety in wet weather, the
eavier airplane needed a firm pavement

Designing an airport is a complex undertaking
that requires matching the needs of the airlines, the aircraft themselves, and the passengers. Runways for intercontinental jet traffic
must be at least 2½ miles (4 km) long and sufficient in number to handle simultaneous takeoffs and landings by different aircraft in changing wind conditions.

Further, an international airport must be
equipped to handle the baggage, local transport, and customs clearance of tens of thousands of passengers daily.

The design below shows the layout and service facilities of Charles de Gaulle airport in
Paris.

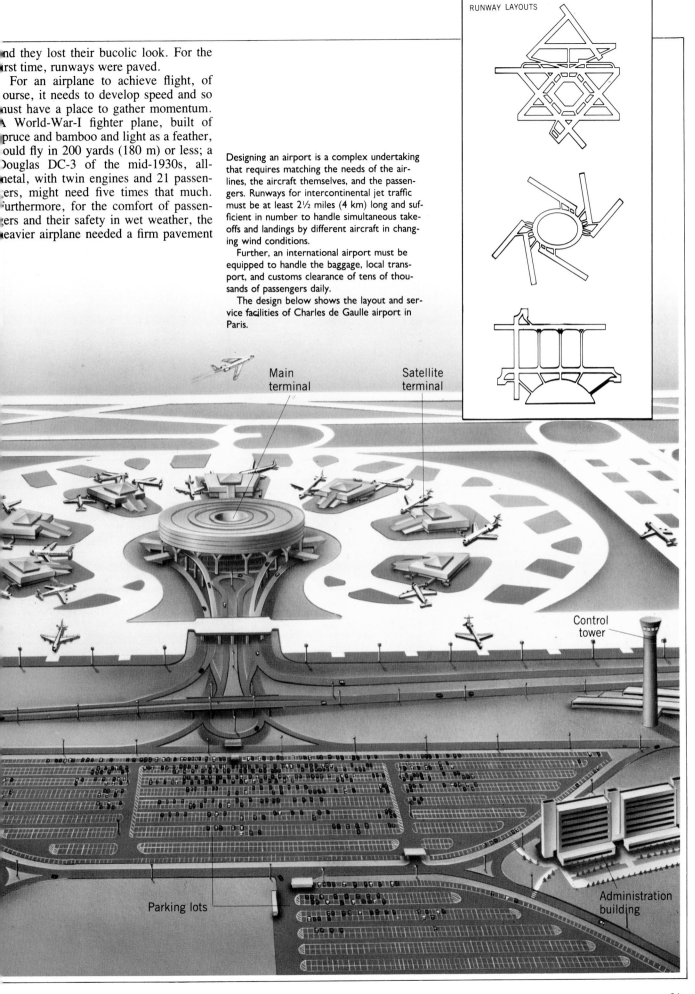

RUNWAY LAYOUTS

Main
terminal

Satellite
terminal

Control
tower

Parking lots

Administration
building

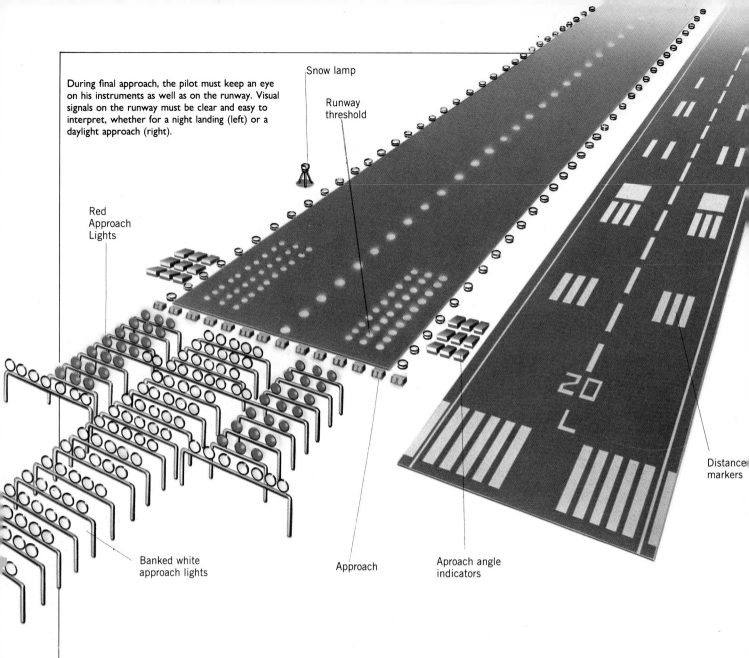

During final approach, the pilot must keep an eye on his instruments as well as on the runway. Visual signals on the runway must be clear and easy to interpret, whether for a night landing (left) or a daylight approach (right).

Snow lamp

Runway threshold

Red Approach Lights

Banked white approach lights

Approach

Aproach angle indicators

Distance markers

20 L

to roll on; in mud, the wheels might easily sink in, causing the plane to nose over.

Because of the effect of wind on moving airplanes, runways had to be laid out in the direction of the most frequently prevailing winds. This is how the typical pattern of an airport evolved, with two or more runways crisscrossing so as to give planes a choice according to which way the wind was blowing, with a large, arrowhead-shaped "wind tee" pointing the direction of the active runway in use at the time.

As passenger traffic increased after World War II, better accommodations had to be provided for the flying public. Not only ticket offices and provisions for handling baggage, but rest rooms, restaurants, and waiting rooms became necessary additions; then, too, facilities had to be provided for the curious who came to see the airplanes taking off and landing. The modern airport, as it grew,

developed a character and appearance all its own.

Time was a vital factor in airport design—the time required to service an airplane after landing, to board a new load of passengers, baggage, and cargo, and to turn the plane around and take off on a new flight. Elaborate boarding ladders were devised that could be rolled up to the plane to get the passengers on and off in a hurry. For baggage, there was everything from conveyor belts to preformed containers that, filled in the terminal, could be rolled up and fitted snugly into the cargo hold of the airplane. Gas trucks were fitted with high-pressure hoses for speedy refilling of tanks. Special cleanup crews whizzed through the cabin to spruce it up for a new crowd. In time, the average turnaround period got as low as 25 minutes, still time enough for passengers who were continuing the flight to stretch their legs in the terminal.

Busiest Airport in the World

In the peacetime years, with passenger traffic growing at the rate of 20 percent yearly, airports could not remain static but had to constantly expand. The challenge to designers was to build an airport that would serve usefully at least for a few years. Chicago's O'Hare, the busiest airport in the world (one airplane landing or taking off every 20 seconds in peak hours), is a prime example. Scarcely was it completed than it was already outdated, and such has been the volume of its traffic that it has never caught up since.

Most airports have suffered, too, from a trend that has tended to move them farther and farther out from the cities they serve, where the residents object to the noise of jumbo jets and supersonic airliners. In most cases, not enough attention has been paid to developing high-speed ways of getting passengers from the city center to the airport. Helicopters are

used, but they only add to the already serious congestion in the air. Ground transportation suffers from traffic jams, so that
it is often necessary to allow as much time
to get to the airport as is required to fly
from the airport to the destination. This is
an area of challenge for airport planners.

With the amount of air traffic that is
normal at most airports serving big cities,
the problem of traffic control has become
one of an airport manager's primary concerns. Not only must incoming traffic be
kept separate from outgoing traffic; in-
bound traffic must be directed into certain

flight channels when it is still many miles
away, and possibly forewarned of the necessity of waiting for some time in a holding pattern before landing. All these
activities are monitored by radar sets supervised by air traffic controllers in a spe-

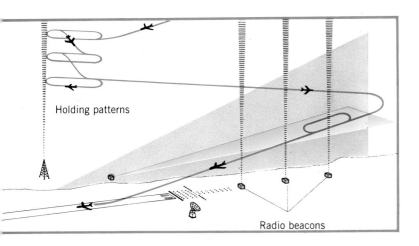

Holding patterns

Radio beacons

Approach, maintaining a holding pattern, and final
landing become more difficult when visibility is
poor. In these circumstances, pilots must depend
on the Instrument Landing System (ILS). The diagram shows how microwave radio beacons help
control ILS landings. The beacon on the far left
gives a reference point to pilots in holding patterns. The three beacons along the final approach
guide the pilot to the correct landing angle. He
must be at a given altitude as he passes through
each microwave beam.

Below: Taxi ramps feeding a main runway.

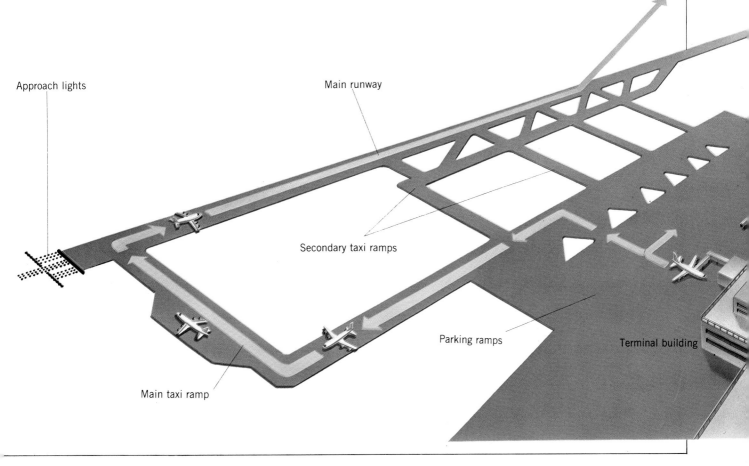

Approach lights

Main runway

Secondary taxi ramps

Parking ramps

Terminal building

Main taxi ramp

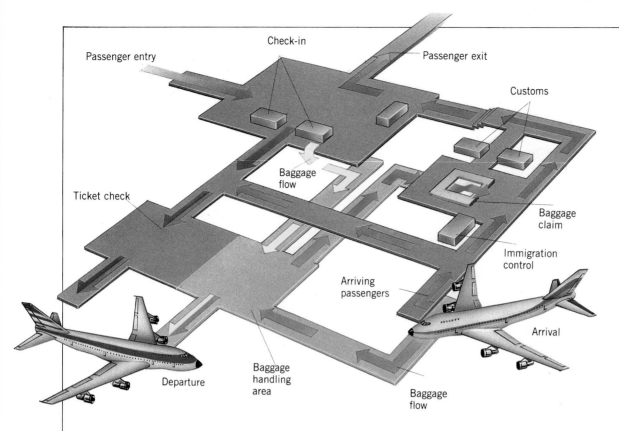

Check-in

Passenger entry

Passenger exit

Customs

Baggage
flow

Ticket check

Baggage
claim

Immigration
control

Arriving
passengers

Arrival

Baggage
handling
area

Departure

Baggage
flow

Diagram of passenger flow in an international airport. Passengers in arrival, in transit, or departure must pass smoothly through customs and immigration control, check-in, baggage claim, etc. These procedures all take time that may partially take away from the advantages of high-speed jet travel.

cially equipped radar room and in the control tower overlooking the field.

Bad-weather landings at large commercial airports today are routine, thanks to an Instrument Landing System (ILS) developed during World War II. The ILS is a system in which an instrument display in the cockpit is coordinated with radio transmitters on the runway. The pilot, guided strictly by the instruments and voice signals from the ground, keeps two needles on a dial crossed and centered. One shows the position of the plane relative to the center of the runway; another shows its angle of descent along an electronic glide path. The pilot brings the aircraft within visual distance of the runway in plenty of time to set it down smoothly and safely. Thus, even the weather has given way to the demands of modern flying, and the airport, home and haven in the days of Huffman's Prairie, remains the same even for the hugest and most sophisticated world-circling airliners.

Two aircraft maintenance vehicles. *Left:* A lift truck for raising food and other inflight supplies to aircraft loading doors. *Right:* A mobile electric generating station, which provides the power to start jet engines or to operate onboard instrumentation when the airplane's motors are shut off.

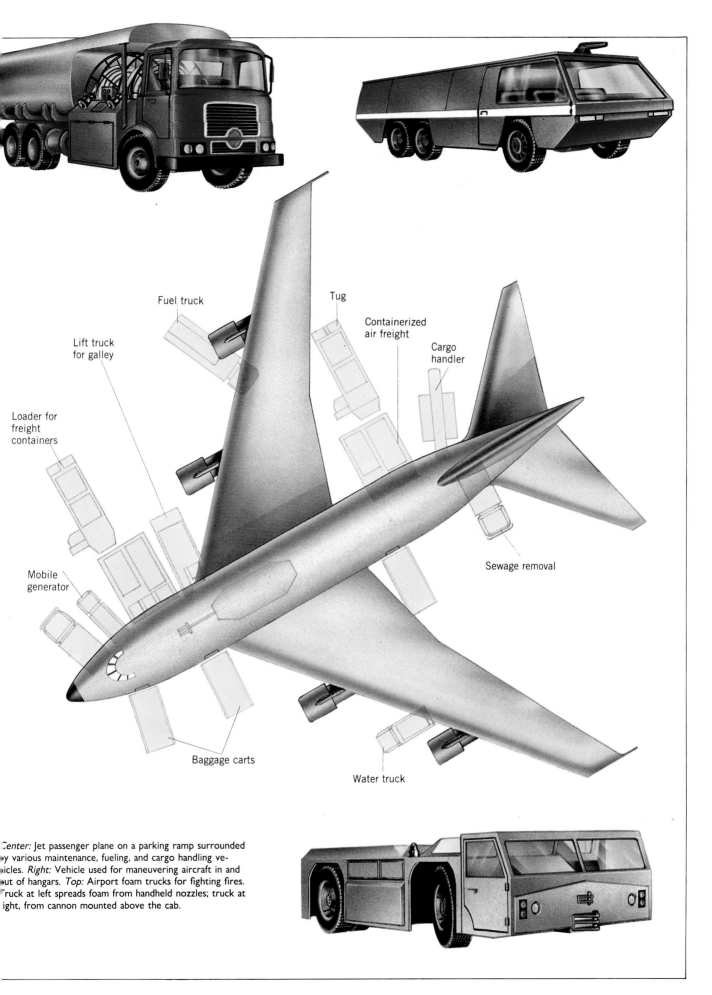

Fuel truck

Lift truck
for galley

Tug

Containerized
air freight

Cargo
handler

Loader for
freight
containers

Sewage removal

Mobile
generator

Baggage carts

Water truck

Center: Jet passenger plane on a parking ramp surrounded
by various maintenance, fueling, and cargo handling vehicles. *Right:* Vehicle used for maneuvering aircraft in and
out of hangars. *Top:* Airport foam trucks for fighting fires.
Truck at left spreads foam from handheld nozzles; truck at
right, from cannon mounted above the cab.

Alarms and Security Systems

Space-age technology has transformed many aspects of our lives in the past few years, but few as dramatically as home protection. Instead of having to rely on watchful neighbors and the old-fashioned policeman on the beat, the modern home-owner has a choice of alarm systems, including ultrasonic and microwave devices. Many alarms are home-protection devices to guard against intruders; others are designed to protect automobiles, offices, or warehouses, while still others signal the presence of smoke, gas, or fire.

The Parts of an Alarm

An alarm system consists of three basic parts—a protective circuit, an output device, and a control circuit. A circuit is simply a complete path for an electric current. An elementary circuit is formed, for instance, by wiring together a battery, a switch, and a light bulb and socket. When the switch is on, there is an uninterrupted flow of current through the wires, and the bulb lights; this circuit is said to be closed. When the switch is off or a wire becomes disconnected, the current ceases to flow, and the bulb does not light; this circuit is said to be open or broken.

The protective circuit is the part of an alarm system that actually does the sleuthing. Many types of protective circuits consist of a small amount of electricity flowing in a closed circuit. When this circuit is broken, the alarm is triggered. Others consist of open circuits that set off the alarm when they are closed. Protective circuits may be designed to trigger an alarm when some action—such as breaking a glass, opening a door or window, a footstep on a carpet, or an object moving in a room—either opens or closes the protective circuit. The protective circuits of other types of alarms may be activated by smoke, gas, or fire.

The output device is the actual alarm signal that is set off when the protective

circuit is activated. Certain output devices are audible, such as bells, horns, or sirens. Others are visible, such as floodlights or strobe lights. Still others are silent and secretly transmit a signal either to a police station or to a special alarm service that monitors the alarm systems of its subscribers.

A control circuit is a relay between the protective circuit and the output device. A relay is a kind of switch that is operated by the flow of current in one circuit (such as the protective circuit) to control the flow of current in another circuit (such as the circuit including the output device). When

Open window or break glass and alarm is triggered

Magnetic sensor signal when door is opened

Photo cell senses change in light levels

Microswitches mounted on door and window frames detect break-in attempts. Other types of sophisticated alarm systems make use of ultrasonic sound waves, infrared light, vibration sensors, and microwaves to detect intruders. Such systems must be carefully tuned to avoid false alarms caused by the rumble of passing traffic, mice, and even flying insects.

Below: Closed-circuit television systems enable one guard to do the work of many, keeping visual control over different security points without ever moving from the monitoring station.

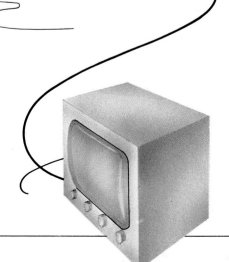

the protective circuit either opens or closes to indicate an alarm, the control circuit relay closes the circuit that activates the output device. A switch in the control circuit allows the alarm system to be shut off and reset when necessary.

Types of Alarms

Space-protection alarms are designed to detect movement such as would be caused by an intruder, in a certain area. Modern space-protection alarms may employ photoelectric, infrared, ultrasonic, or microwave devices.

Photoelectric alarms send an invisible beam of light from a transmitter to a receiver. These two parts are usually placed on either side of a door or corridor where an intruder is likely to pass. When the beam is in normal operation, the protective circuit is closed, and no alarm is sounded. If an intruder should step in the way, the beam is interrupted, the circuit is suddenly broken, and the alarm is triggered.

Infrared alarms rely on the fact that all objects—walls and furniture as well as human beings—emit a certain amount of

Open door triggers alarm

Siren

Vibration sensor

Infrared photo cells

Closed-circuit TV

sound waves. Sound waves are produced by the vibration of air molecules. The number of vibrations per second is called the frequency of the sound. The human ear can hear frequencies of between about 20 and 20,000 vibrations per second. Sound waves with frequencies above that are called ultrasonic (*see* ULTRASOUND). These alarms generate ultrasonic waves and "listen" to them as they bounce or "echo" off objects in the protected area. A moving object—such as an intruder—will cause the frequency of the waves that bounce off it to change. Any ultrasonic alarm is designed to listen for small changes in the frequency of the sound waves it emits and to trigger an alarm when it hears one.

While ultrasonic alarms employ high-frequency sound waves, microwave alarms employ high-frequency radio waves (*see* MICROWAVE). Extremely high-frequency radio waves, or microwaves, echo off walls, floors, and objects just as do ultrasonic waves. Furthermore, the frequencies of these waves change slightly when they bounce off moving objects, just as in the case of ultrasonic waves. A microwave alarm is designed to trigger an alarm whenever such changes in the frequencies of the waves it produces are detected.

infrared energy, or heat (for more information on this effect, *see* INFRARED RADIATION). This amount remains relatively constant, changing very slowly even if the temperature of the room should rise or fall. An infrared alarm is designed to monitor the amount of heat normally radiated by objects in a protected area, called the background radiation, and to watch for sudden changes. If an intruder should enter the protected area, the small but sudden change in the background radiation is sufficient to set off the alarm.

Ultrasonic alarms are also designed to detect changes, but in the frequency of

Different kinds of alarm systems are available to protect automobiles from car thieves. One type blocks current from reaching the ignition system. Others detect vibrations caused by attempted break-in and honk the horn or set off an alarm siren. Some systems combine both an ignition block and an acoustic alarm.

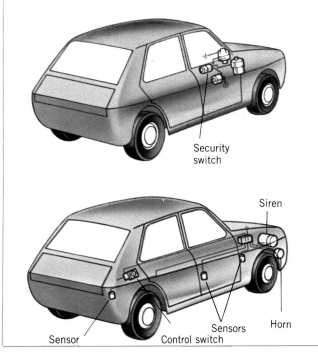

Security switch

Siren

Sensor

Sensors

Control switch

Horn

Alcohol Consumption

Of all the wide variety of drugs that people have used throughout history to change their moods or their behavior, none is more pervasive—or more abused—than alcohol. The Bible tells how Noah got drunk after the Flood, and countless drinkers have been following his example ever since. Cocaine, heroin, and marijuana may readily come to people's minds when drug addiction is discussed, but alcohol, when it comes to hard facts, outstrips all of these in steady and addictive use.

What is meant by alcohol here is chemically known as ethyl alcohol, or ethanol (formula: CH_3CH_2OH), which is found in beer, wine, whiskey, gin, vodka, brandy, and other drinks manufactured by man, including an almost infinite variety of cocktails. The percentage of alcohol in

The rate of absorption of alcohol depends upon the water content of the various organs, which is one reason why it is a quick-acting drug. Not much is concentrated in fatty or muscle tissue; far more is absorbed by the brain. If a drinker takes a lot of alcohol in a short time, a relatively large amount will be passed quickly to the brain. This produces a rapid "high," a stage of early intoxication that makes the drinker feel euphoric and excitable. This stage does not last long. Alcohol is not only absorbed quickly, it is also disposed of quickly. A tiny amount disappears almost at once, being exhaled through the lungs and excreted as sweat. Somewhat more is handled by the kidneys and disposed of in the urine. About 90 percent is eliminated by metabolic processes, mostly in the liver.

sized person who drinks 4 ounces (about 120 ml) of 100-proof (50-percent alcohol) whiskey per hour will begin to get drunk fairly soon. This drinker will have 1.5 ounces (44 cc) of alcohol in his body at the end of an hour, a blood concentration of 0.07 percent. At this point, he feels "high." After 2 hours of drinking, he will have 0.11 percent—enough to be found legally intoxicated in most places in the world.

Drink Long and Slow

If he does not drink at this fast a rate, intoxication will take longer. At the end of each hour, the alcohol concentration in the blood drops slightly; further drinking, however, lifts it to a higher level. Thus, a person who drinks only small amounts over a relatively long period will not have

Alcoholic beverages vary in chemical composition and caloric content, depending on the ingredients used and the fermenting process followed. The major component of wine and liquor is alcohol. Beer has a greater proportion of proteins and sugars. The caloric content of wine comes mainly from ethyl alcohol, while the caloric content of sweet wines and liquors is from sugar. Although wine and liquor produce the same effect on the body, liquor is more irritating to the digestive system.

COMPOSITION OF VARIOUS ALCOHOLIC BEVERAGES (per 100 cc)	Alcohol (grams)	Proteins (grams)	Fats (grams)	Carbohydrates (grams)	Calories	Calcium (milligrams)
Dark beer	2.24	0.3	trace	3.0	28	6.8
Light beer	3.34	0.3	trace	2.0	32	9.5
Dry cider	3.78	trace	0	2.6	37	8.0
Sweet cider	3.68	trace	0	4.3	42	8.0
Beaujolais	9.44	trace	0	0.3	67	7.5
Champagne	9.85	trace	0	1.4	74	3.5
Red chianti	9.12	trace	0	0.2	65	3.0
Red port	15.06	trace	0	11.4	152	4.7
Liquor, 70 proof, brandy, gin, rum, whiskey	31.05	0	0	trace	222	trace

these drinks ranges from about 2 percent (in light beer) to as high as 50 percent in some vodkas, rums, and liqueurs, which are among the strongest drinks popularly consumed.

A Fast Worker

One of the reasons why people like to use alcohol is that it acts quickly to produce the desired effect. Alcohol does not have to go through a process of digestion: it can be, and is, diffused directly into the bloodstream and from there all over the body. The process may begin in the mouth, where a very small part is diluted by the saliva. It is continued in the stomach, where a small portion is diffused through the stomach wall. It then passes into the small intestine, where it is rapidly absorbed. Once in the bloodstream, the alcohol is circulated to various organs, chief among these in importance being the liver and the brain.

Enzyme Actions

This 90 percent is the most important portion of the alcohol consumed. What happens to it? First, it is acted upon by enzyme alcohol dehydrogenase, which is produced in the liver cells. This enzyme converts it to acetaldehyde, a poison that is quickly rendered harmless by another enzyme, aldehyde dehydrogenase. It is then converted to acetate, which is absorbed by the bloodstream. This is the only phase in which alcohol acts as a nutrient, furnishing about 200 calories of energy per ounce of alcohol consumed.

The reason why alcohol consumption so often results in intoxication, or drunkenness, is that there is a limit on the rate at which the body can dispose of it. If a drinker quaffs alcohol faster than it can be metabolized, then, of course, it begins to accumulate in one or another of the body's organs, chiefly in the brain and in the liver, which absorb it most readily. An average-

any serious intoxicating effects from it.

The effects of drinking a lot of alcohol in a relatively short time are well known: dizziness, impaired vision, nausea, etc. Alcohol affects the central nervous system; it acts, like a barbiturate, as a depressant. Its effect is two-phased. In the beginning, it is like a mild tranquilizer, making drinkers euphoric or excited, diminishing their inhibitions. Once this phase is over, it is all downhill. Most drinkers become morose, silent, sedated, and stuporous; they finally pass out. The first excited phase is caused by suppression of those brain centers that normally inhibit extreme behavior. The ensuing dizziness, slurred speech, and staggering are the result of a similar suppression of the brain centers controlling speech and motor activities. By "putting the brakes" on the controlling areas of the brain, an effect on the muscles is produced.

QUANTITIES OF ALCOHOLIC SUBSTANCES EQUIVALENT IN CALORIC CONTENT TO RED AND WHITE TABLE WINES (10%) (20 G OF ALCOHOL = 140 CALORIES)

GRAMS

30 40 50 60 70 80 90 100 110 120 130 140

White and red table wines — 200

Very dry wine

Very sweet wine

Beer — 400

Liqueur

Marsala

Vermouth

Aperitif

Whiskey

Kummel

Anisette

Gin

Acqua vita

Cognac

In many countries, blood tests are required for drivers suspected of being drunk. There is no agreement on what percentage of alcohol in the blood constitutes intoxication. This seems to be different for different people. There are steady, heavy drinkers who are able to absorb quite a lot of alcohol before their functions become impaired. This is an indication of the addictive qualities of alcohol, in that it takes more and more to achieve the desired state of intoxication. In general, intoxication starts at about 0.15 percent of alcohol in the blood. At 0.3 percent, even hardened drinkers will begin to show some signs of being drunk. At 0.4 percent, the average person will be so anesthetized that he will feel no pain if surgery is performed upon him—a fact often put into practice before the discovery of general anesthesia. By 0.5 percent,

AVERAGE DAILY INTAKE OF WINE AND LIQUOR

21 ounces (620 ml) of wine (10%)
3-4 glasses

18 ounces (530 ml) of wine (12%)

17 ounces (500 ml) of wine (10%) plus 1 ounce (30 ml) of liquor (40 percent)

8.5 ounces (250 ml) of wine (10%) plus 3 ounces (90 ml) of liquor (40 percent)

A normal healthy person should not consume more than about 1.75 ounces by weight (50 g) of alcohol per day. This provides approximately 350 calories, but alcohol cannot be used as a substitute for other nutrients. The table at left lists the amounts of wine and liquor which can be eliminated by the body in a 24-hour period, the equivalent of about 1.75 ounces (50 g) of absolute alcohol).

the drinker is in danger of dying because the heart may be anesthetized to the degree that it no longer functions, or the brain centers controlling breathing may stop working so that asphyxiation results.

Accidents and the DTs

Alcohol also has an effect on the highest brain functions: thinking, learning, remembering, and making judgments. These are perhaps the most serious of all its effects. Fuzzy thinking can turn a harmless quarrel into an argument that will not stop short of violence. Making judgments may involve many people if the drinker is driving a car and misjudges a tight situation. A drunken person is more than usually accident-prone—as much as seven times as accident-prone as the normal population. Brain diseases, malnutrition, delirium tremens, and sudden, violent, apparently maniacal fits may also result from chronic alcohol consumption. Cirrhosis of the liver is a classic symptom of the disease of alcoholism, one that cannot be reversed or retarded unless the person stops drinking entirely. In general, the life expectancy of alcoholics is reduced by 10 or 12 years.

The most difficult aspect of alcohol consumption is the fact that it is traditionally an acceptable social practice. The cocaine snorter, the heroin user, even the occasional marijuana smoker are engaging in practices that the law, for the most part, does not tolerate; they are therefore generally liable to social censure as well. But as for alcohol, few attempts have ever been made to put it beyond the law. The Eighteenth Amendment to the U.S. Constitution outlawed the manufacture, transport, and sale of alcohol. The consequences of Prohibition in rising crime rates, and the continuation of prohibited drinking by anyone who could afford bootlegged liquor, were so severe that the Amendment was repealed in 1933, after only 14 years.

Modest quantities of alcohol can be digested and eliminated by the body without difficulty. The liver is the major site of blood purification. It is composed of functional units called liver lobules, which are responsible for the removal of various wastes from the blood and for the breakdown of certain toxic substances. After digestion, alcohol is broken down to carbon dioxide and water. The rate of elimination of alcohol from the blood and an individual's tolerance for alcohol vary, but prolonged high consumption inevitably reduces the liver's effectiveness in removal of wastes. High consumption of alcohol can lead to cirrhosis of the liver and many other health problems associated with alcoholism.

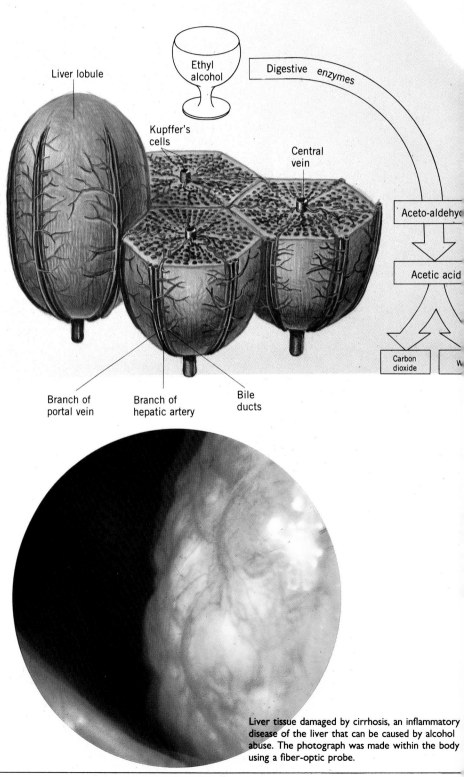

Liver lobule

Ethyl alcohol

Digestive enzymes

Kupffer's cells

Central vein

Aceto-aldehyde

Acetic acid

Carbon dioxide

W

Branch of portal vein

Branch of hepatic artery

Bile ducts

Liver tissue damaged by cirrhosis, an inflammatory disease of the liver that can be caused by alcohol abuse. The photograph was made within the body using a fiber-optic probe.

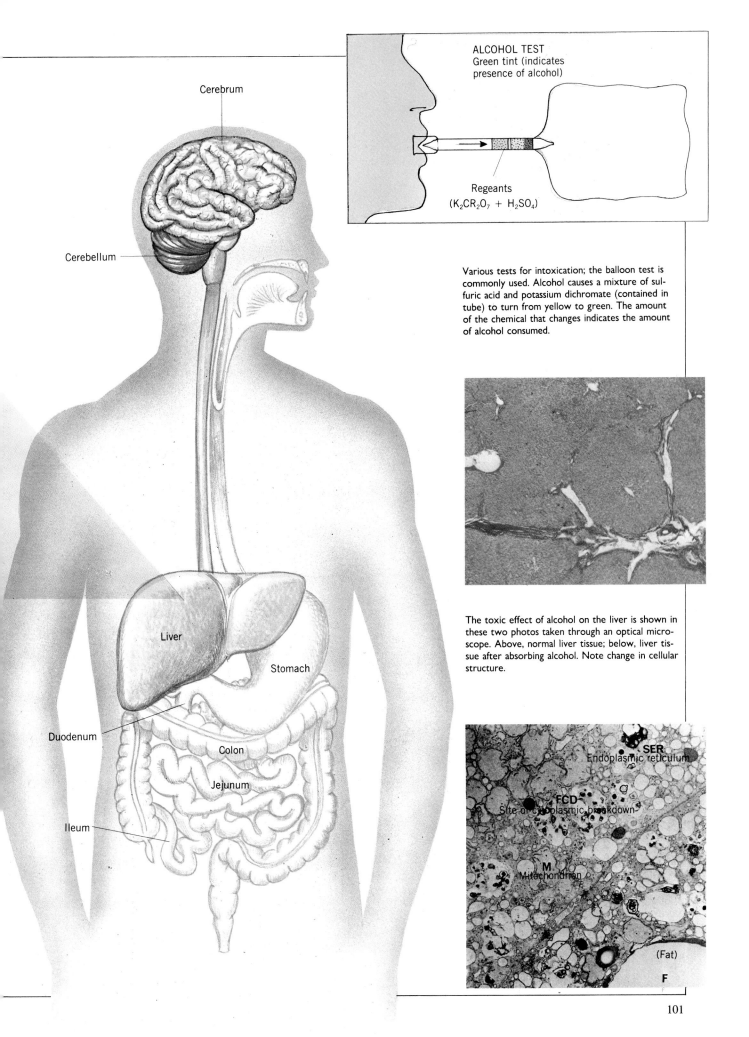

Cerebrum

Cerebellum

Liver

Stomach

Duodenum

Colon

Jejunum

Ileum

ALCOHOL TEST
Green tint (indicates
presence of alcohol)

Regeants
($K_2CR_2O_7 + H_2SO_4$)

Various tests for intoxication; the balloon test is commonly used. Alcohol causes a mixture of sulfuric acid and potassium dichromate (contained in tube) to turn from yellow to green. The amount of the chemical that changes indicates the amount of alcohol consumed.

The toxic effect of alcohol on the liver is shown in these two photos taken through an optical microscope. Above, normal liver tissue; below, liver tissue after absorbing alcohol. Note change in cellular structure.

SER
Endoplasmic reticulum

FCD
Site of cytoplasmic breakdown

M
Mitochondrion

(Fat)

F

Alcohols

The word "alcohol" suggests to most people either rubbing alcohol or the alcohol in wine, beer, and whiskey. The former, wood alcohol, is highly poisonous when mistaken for the latter, grain alcohol, the intoxicating (and somewhat poisonous) ingredient in drinks. The chemist calls them methyl and ethyl alcohol, respectively, and they are the first and lightest in a long series of alcohols, which have many scientific and industrial uses.

Because some alcohols freeze only at extremely low temperatures, they make excellent antifreeze compounds for use in automobile radiators. Others, with heavy molecular structures, may be viscous liquids like glycerine or solids like cholesterol, two compounds familiar to everyone but probably not ordinarily thought of as alcohols.

All alcohols have two things in common—their close relationship to a class of organic chemical compounds called hydrocarbons, and the presence in each of them of a group made up of one atom of oxygen combined with one of hydrogen. Such a group is called a radical, and in chemical reactions, it acts as a unit.

A hydrocarbon is simply a chemical compound whose molecule is made up of atoms of carbon and hydrogen and nothing else. To understand hydrocarbons, it is necessary to become familiar with just a few basic facts about that phenomenal chemical element, carbon. Known to most people in its two pure forms as charcoal and diamond, carbon differs from all other elements because its atoms are able to link up with each other to form carbon chains, some of which are extremely long and to which other elements and radicals can attach themselves to make organic compounds. Outnumbering all the compounds of all the other elements, organic compounds often exist in series that differ one from the other in distinct ways.

Saturated Hydrocarbons

One of the basic series includes hundreds of compounds known as saturated hydrocarbons. Each carbon atom has four "links" to which other atoms can be attached to form new substances. When each of the links not involved in forming the carbon chain itself is attached to a hydrogen atom, then the compound is said to be saturated. When one of the hydrogen atoms is replaced by a hydroxyl (OH) group, then you have an alcohol.

The saturated hydrocarbons make up a regular and very simple series so far as the structure of its members is concerned. The series begins with methane, which is the principal component of the gas used in a kitchen stove. Methane is made up of one atom of carbon linked to four atoms of hydrogen. Chemists write its empirical

When a hydroxyl group (OH) is substituted for a hydrogen atom in a hydrocarbon, an alcohol is formed. An alcohol containing more than one hydroxyl is called a polyhydroxyl alcohol. At normal temperatures, alcohols are liquid and are extremely soluble in water because they form hydrogen bonds.

ALCOHOLS	R—OH	P.EB. °C	SOLUBIL g/l H₂O
Methyl alcohol (methanol)	CH_3OH	64.5	∞
Ethyl alcohol (ethanol)	$CH_3—CH_2—OH$	78.3	∞
Propyl alcohol (propanol)	$CH_3—CH_2—CH_2OH$	97	∞
Butyl alcohol (butanol)	$CH_3—CH_2—CH_2—CH_2—OH$	118	79
Pentyl alcohol (pentanol)	$CH_3—CH_2—CH_2—CH_2—CH_2OH$	138	23
Dodecanol	$CH_3—(CH_2)_{10}—CH_2—OH$	—	—
Ethylene glycol	CH₂—OH / CH₂—OH	197	∞
Glycerine (glycerol)	CH₂—OH / CH—OH / CH₂—OH	290	∞
Benzyl alcohol	(ring)—CH₂—OH	205	40
Cholesterol	(steroid structure)	—	—

∞ = in tutte le proporzioni

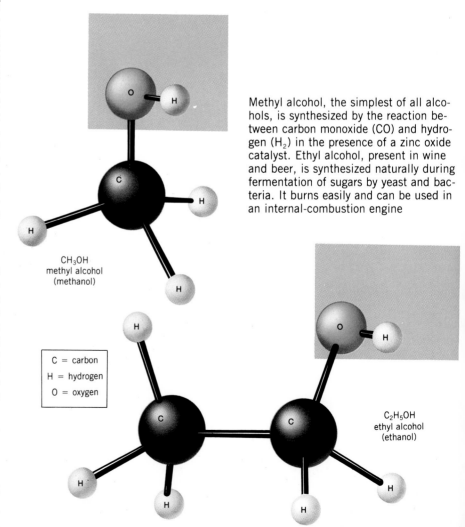

C = carbon
H = hydrogen
O = oxygen

CH₃OH
methyl alcohol
(methanol)

C₂H₅OH
ethyl alcohol
(ethanol)

Methyl alcohol, the simplest of all alcohols, is synthesized by the reaction between carbon monoxide (CO) and hydrogen (H_2) in the presence of a zinc oxide catalyst. Ethyl alcohol, present in wine and beer, is synthesized naturally during fermentation of sugars by yeast and bacteria. It burns easily and can be used in an internal-combustion engine

formula (the symbols of the elements with numbers showing how many atoms of each element are in the molecule) as CH_4. Its structural formula is given below, together with that of the second member of the series, which is ethane (empirical formula C_2H_6):

H H H
| | |
H—C—H   H—C—C—H
| | |
H H H
methane   *ethane*

The empirical formulas for the saturated hydrocarbons follow a beautifully simple mathematical formula, which can be expressed as $C_nH_{(2n+2)}$. Since the n represents the number of carbon atoms in the hydrocarbon, the formula shows that each higher hydrocarbon has twice as many atoms (plus two) of hydrogen as it has atoms of carbon.

We have said that the alcohols are made by replacing one of the hydrogen atoms of a saturated hydrocarbon by an OH (hydroxyl) group. Let us take a look at the structural formulas for the three lightest alcohols, which are derived, respectively, from the three lightest hydrocarbons:

H   H H
| | |
H—C—OH   H—C—C—OH
| | |
H   H H
methyl alcohol   *ethyl alcohol*

H H H
| | |
H—C—C—C—OH
| | |
H H H
propyl alcohol

Chemists have a third type of formula, which is halfway between an empirical formula and a structural formula. These formulas give a pretty good idea of how the molecule is made up by listing the parts of the structural formula. Thus, for ethyl alcohol, C_2H_5OH, we can write CH_3CH_2OH, and for propyl alcohol, C_3H_7OH, we can express the formula as $CH_3CH_2CH_2OH$, and it is clear that the molecule is made up of a CH_3 group followed by a certain number of CH_2 groups and an OH group.

Some alcohols are good examples of the phenomenon known as isomerism. Isomers are compounds with identical empirical formulas but with different structural formulas. When a saturated hydrocarbon like propane takes on an OH group to form an alcohol, the new group can replace either an end hydrogen atom or a central one, thus forming one of two possible propyl alcohols, which have these structural formulas:

H H H
| | |
H—C—C—C—OH
| | |
H H H
n-propyl alcohol

H H H
| | |
H—C—C—C—H
| | |
H OH H
isopropyl alcohol

Notice the prefixes n- (for normal) and iso- (for isomeric), in these names, which are the names that chemists might use in talking about the products. In formal writing, they would use the official names, which were chosen in 1957 at a Paris conference of the International Union of Pure and Applied Chemistry. This conference revised the rules governing the naming of organic compounds in an effort to get all chemists the world over to use the same names. Until then, the lightest alcohol was known by such various names, including wood alcohol, methyl alcohol, carbinol, and methanol. The second lightest was known as grain alcohol, ethyl alcohol, ethanol, and methylcarbinol, this last being a particularly confusing name. As an example of what the IUPAC delegates accomplished, here are the official names for the first four alcohols, in the series: methanol, ethanol, propanol (with its isomer, 2-propanol), 2-buten-1-ol. The 2 in 2-propanol means that the OH group is attached to the second carbon atom in the formula.

Polyhedric Alcohols

Sometimes, more than one hydrogen atom in a hydrocarbon can be replaced by an OH group. The compounds thus formed are called polyhedric alcohols. An example is ethylene glycol, which is familiar as an antifreeze for automobile radiators. It is very soluble in water, and it does not corrode the metal in car radiators; in addition, it has both a low freezing point and a high boiling point, which means that it does not boil away during hot weather. The simplest compound with three OH groups replacing hydrogen is glycerol, a thick, viscous alcohol commonly known as glycerine, which has many uses besides healing chapped lips and serving as artificial tears for movie actresses. The structural formulas of these two polyhedric alcohols are:

H H
| |
H—C—C—C
| |
OH OH
ethylene glycol

H H H
| | |
H—C—C—C—H
| | |
OH OH OH
glycerol

Alcohols are very useful in industry either as themselves or as intermediate substances for the preparation of other chemicals. The lower alcohols—that is, the lighter ones, which are derived from the first few members of the saturated hydrocarbon series—are useful not only as components of antifreeze formulas for automobiles but also as solvents and extractants (that is, agents for separating out components of another substance).

The lower alcohols—the ones with no more than three carbon atoms in the chain—are soluble in water, and all monohydroxyl alcohols—those with only one OH group—are soluble in organic solvents. The ones containing fewer than 12 carbon atoms in the chain are liquid at room temperature; those with 12 or more are solids. Polyhedric alcohols (glycerine is an example) usually take the form of syrups. Some alcohols with a large number of carbon atoms in the chain are very complex in composition and usually are solid at room temperature. This is the case with the sterols, including cholesterol, the one that may aggravate certain health problems if intake and elimination are not properly balanced.

When Alcohols React as Bases

When they react with acids, alcohols, because of the presence of the hydroxyl radical, perform as bases. (For the general conditions of acid-base reactions, *see* ACIDS AND BASES). The product of an acid-alcohol reaction is known as an ester. A simple example is the reaction between acetic acid and ethanol (ethyl alcohol), in which the final products are the ester, ethyl acetate, and water. Ethyl acetate is used as a solvent. If acetic acid is allowed to react with methanol, it yields a fragrant ester, which is used in making perfumes.

Some reactions between alcohols and acids are reversible under certain conditions, and so an ester can be made to react with water to form an alcohol and an acid.

Inorganic compounds containing the OH group are called hydroxides, and when a hydroxide is heated together with certain esters, the esters decompose to yield soap and glycerine—the process known as saponification. Common fats and oils are mixtures of esters such as stearin, made from stearic acid and glycerol, and palmitin, made from palmitic acid and glycerol.

See also ACIDS AND BASES; CHEMICAL BOND AND VALENCE.

Aldehydes and Ketones

One of those crawly creatures known as a millipede ("thousand-legger"), a species hardly longer than its scientific name, *Apheloria corrugata,* has an interesting way of polishing off its enemies. When cornered, this sly "bug" injects a type of protein called an enzyme into a sac within its body. The enzyme sets off a chemical process in which a substance called benzaldehyde cyanohydrin is formed, and this immediately breaks down into two products, an innocent chemical, benzaldehyde, and a deadly gas, hydrogen cyanide (which is the fatally poisonous gas released by the cyanide pellets in a prison gas chamber). The millipede positions its body so that the sac is pointed at its tormentor and ejects the hydrogen cyanide, which can kill a small enemy on the spot. The benzaldehyde, on the other hand, is the same chemical compound from which vanillin is made, the substance used by many ice cream manufacturers to produce their vanilla-flavored products.

Benzaldehyde is one of a group of chemical compounds known as aldehydes. (A compound is the substance formed when atoms of two or more chemical elements join together to form a product; the product may be quite unlike any of the elements in it, as when two gases, hydrogen and oxygen, combine to form the liquid we know as water; *see* CHEMICAL BOND AND VALENCE). Aldehydes and a similar group of compounds called ketones are distinguished by the presence of a carbon-oxygen group called the carbonyl group, which chemists write in their shorthand as:

In aldehydes, of the two carbon bonds not linked to the oxygen, at least one is linked to a hydrogen atom (ketones may have both carbon bonds taken up by groups). (Before reading about any group of compounds containing carbon, which are the compounds studied in organic chemistry, it is worthwhile first to *see* HYDROCARBONS, which explains how carbon atoms link together to form chains or rings.) In what are called straight-chain hydrocarbons, each of the carbon atoms is joined to two hydrogen atoms, except for the carbon atoms at the ends of the chains, which are joined to three hydrogen atoms. For example, when four carbon atoms are joined with ten hydrogen atoms, butane is formed. This is a gas used in most cigarette lighters, and the formula for it is written:

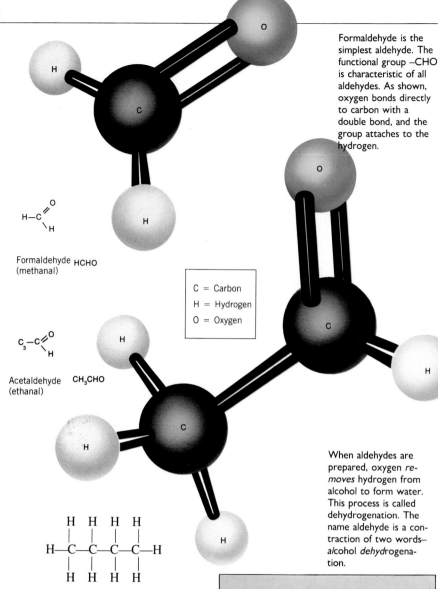

Formaldehyde HCHO
(methanal)

Acetaldehyde CH₃CHO
(ethanal)

C = Carbon
H = Hydrogen
O = Oxygen

Formaldehyde is the simplest aldehyde. The functional group –CHO is characteristic of all aldehydes. As shown, oxygen bonds directly to carbon with a double bond, and the group attaches to the hydrogen.

When aldehydes are prepared, oxygen *removes* hydrogen from alcohol to form water. This process is called dehydrogenation. The name aldehyde is a contraction of two words— *alco*hol *dehydr*ogenation.

If two of the hydrogen atoms in the end positions are replaced by a single oxygen atom, the resulting compound is the aldehyde known as butanal, with this formula:

If the carbon atom linked to the oxygen atom is not also linked to a hydrogen atom—that is, if the carbon atom is linked

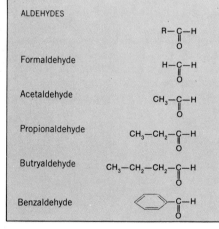

ALDEHYDES	
	R—C—H, O
Formaldehyde	H—C—H, O
Acetaldehyde	CH₃—C—H, O
Propionaldehyde	CH₃—CH₂—C—H, O
Butyraldehyde	CH₃—CH₂—CH₂—C—H, O
Benzaldehyde	—C—H, O

INDUSTRIAL SYNTHESIS

Formic aldehyde

Methyl alcohol → Cu (copper) catalyst → Formaldehyde + H₂ (Catalytic dehydrogenation of methyl alcohol)

Uses: Formaldehyde + Phenol → Bakelite; Urea → Urea resin; Melamine → Melamine resin; Casein → Galatite

Acetaldehyde

Ethylene + Oxygen (CH₂=CH₂ + ½O₂) → CuCl₂ catalyst → Acetaldehyde (CH₃—C=O) (Catalytic oxidation of ethylene)

Uses: Acetaldehyde — Preparation of acetic acid intermediate for: Synthetic rubber, Plastics, Explosives, Pharmaceuticals

only to oxygen and to two other carbon atoms—then the compound is a ketone (and just as aldehydes have names ending in -al, all ketones have names ending in -one).

The simplest aldehyde is methanal. It is formed from the simplest hydrocarbon, methane, and is familiar to most people under its common name, formaldehyde. Formaldehyde is widely used in tanning leather and as a preservative (it is an important ingredient of embalming fluid). Ethanal, the second in the series of aldehydes (corresponding to the hydrocarbon ethane), also has a common name by which it is better known, acetaldehyde. This compound finds its chief use in industry as an intermediate product in the synthesis, or making of other compounds such as chloral, which also contains chlorine and is used in the manufacture of the pesticide DDT. Another derivative of chloral, chloral hydrate, used to be known as "knockout drops" because it was the active ingredient of the Mickey Finn, a drink secretly foisted on victims whom an enemy wanted to put to sleep in a hurry (the technique is similar to, although less lethal than, the one used on its enemies by the millipede).

The simplest ketone is acetone, and like many of the ketones, it is used mostly as a solvent; it is familiar to most people in the form of nail polish remover. One of the more complicated ketones, cyclohexanone, is used in manufacturing building units for complex polymers, including nylon.

Aside from the picturesque applications of aldehydes and ketones mentioned above, these two classes of organic compounds are of vital importance in the chemical industry. Without them, the world would be quite different from what it is today, since there is scarcely a manufacturing process involving chemical compounds that does not make use of these two groups.

Formaldehyde, acetaldehyde, and acetone are very important in the chemical industry: the first two serve as intermediates; acetone serves as a solvent. Illustrated is the molecule of camphor, a familiar ketone.

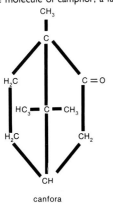

canfora

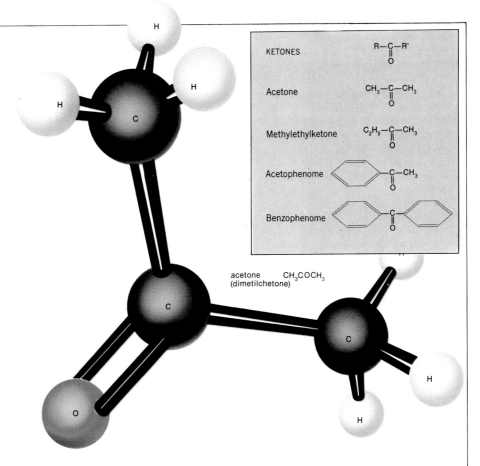

KETONES	$R-\underset{\underset{O}{\parallel}}{C}-R'$
Acetone	$CH_3-\underset{\underset{O}{\parallel}}{C}-CH_3$
Methylethylketone	$C_2H_5-\underset{\underset{O}{\parallel}}{C}-CH_3$
Acetophenome	$C-CH_3$
Benzophenome	C

acetone CH_3COCH_3
(dimetilchetone)

The substitution of hydrogen of the —CHO group of acetaldehyde with a carbon atom bonded to three other hydrogens (CH_3) forms acetone (dimethylketone). The functional group of ketones is the carbonyl group (—CO—). However, instead of being bonded to a hydrogen atom, it is bonded to two other carbon atoms. Aldehydes are derived from primary alcohols structured as R—CH_2OH by the removal of two hydrogen atoms. Ketones are derived from secondary alcohols structured R—CHOH—R'.

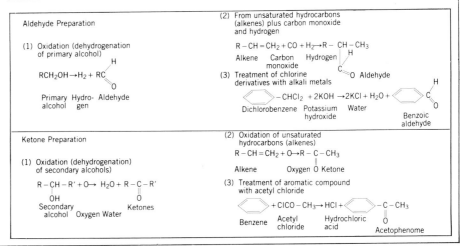

INDUSTRIAL SYNTHESIS

$$CH_3-CH=CH_2+H_2O \longrightarrow CH_3-\underset{\underset{OH}{|}}{CH}-CH_3 \xrightarrow[Cat.]{ZnO} CH_3-\underset{\underset{O}{\parallel}}{C}-CH_3 +H_2$$

Propylene   Water   Isopropyl alcohol   Acetone   Hydrogen

Uses   Acetone { Solvents / Epoxy resins / Plexiglass

Aldehyde Preparation

(1) Oxidation (dehydrogenation of primary alcohol)

$$RCH_2OH \rightarrow H_2 + RC\underset{O}{\overset{H}{<}}$$

Primary   Hydro-   Aldehyde
alcohol   gen

(2) From unsaturated hydrocarbons (alkenes) plus carbon monoxide and hydrogen

$$R-CH=CH_2+CO+H_2 \rightarrow R-\underset{\underset{C<_O^H}{|}}{CH}-CH_3$$

Alkene   Carbon   Hydrogen
monoxide   Aldehyde

(3) Treatment of chlorine derivatives with alkali metals

$$-CHCl_2+2KOH \rightarrow 2KCl+H_2O+ C<_O^H$$

Dichlorobenzene   Potassium   Water   Benzoic
hydroxide   aldehyde

Ketone Preparation

(1) Oxidation (dehydrogenation) of secondary alcohols

$$R-\underset{\underset{OH}{|}}{CH}-R'+O \rightarrow H_2O+R-\underset{\underset{O}{\parallel}}{C}-R'$$

Secondary   Oxygen   Water   Ketones
alcohol

(2) Oxidation of unsaturated hydrocarbons (alkenes)

$$R-CH=CH_2+O \rightarrow R-\underset{\underset{O}{\parallel}}{C}-CH_3$$

Alkene   Oxygen O   Ketone

(3) Treatment of aromatic compound with acetyl chloride

$$+ClCO-CH_3 \rightarrow HCl+ -\underset{\underset{O}{\parallel}}{C}-CH_3$$

Benzene   Acetyl   Hydrochloric
chloride   acid   Acetophenome

Algae

Some species of algae are so useful to human beings that they are being considered for space voyages. A limited amount of certain types of these plants can supply astronauts with oxygen to breathe and at the same time consume all the carbon dioxide waste from their breathing and generate new, high-quality protein that astronauts can eat.

What Algae Are

Algae are primitive plants lacking true roots, stems, or leaves. They number more than 25,000 varieties and virtually cover the Earth, living in soil, wood, hot springs, treetops, on snow crystals and turtles' backs, at the bottom of lagoons, and along coral reefs and rocky coasts. Most algae live in the ocean and compose the various plants we think of as seaweed.

Algae fossils have been found that are more ancient than the dinosaur, dating as far back as 3,000 million years. The wide variety of algae currently alive are divided into three major groups: Chlorophyta, Phaeophyta, and Rhodophyta, which are green, brown, and red. The green Chlorophyta are the most abundant and named for their possession of chlorophyll, the substance responsible for photosynthesis, as explained below. Unlike the self-feeding autotrophic green algae, the red and brown algae are heterotrophic, obtaining their nourishment from other sources. Algae may be single or multicelled. Many are too small to see, but one form of the brown variety, kelp, can measure up to 200 feet (70 m) in length.

Algae and Photosynthesis

Algae and other plants derive energy from sunlight to combine water, carbon dioxide, and minerals into organic matter such as carbohydrates. During daylight hours, they also generate a waste product in the form of oxygen, but after dark, their respiration liberates a relatively small amount of carbon dioxide. Through this process of photosynthesis, plants with chlorophyll provide the Earth with the oxygen needed to sustain almost every form of animal life. The most powerful of all photosynthetic agents, by virtue of their abundance, are algae that grow in water. These aquatic plants are responsible for approximately 90 percent of the oxygen supply of the planet.

Algae and the Food Cycle

Because algae and other plants do not depend on other life forms for food, they are considered primary producers, meaning that they are the beginning of a series of nutrient relays called the food chain. Secondary food-chain links are creatures such as fish, animals, and mammals, which get their energy by consuming plants and animals. In addition to being main providers for their environment, or ecosystem, algae are also garbage collectors, constantly absorbing chemical and mineral wastes produced by respiration and the decay of dead organic and inorganic matter. Since carbon dioxide is the waste product of our own breathing and the respiration of all animals, the algae

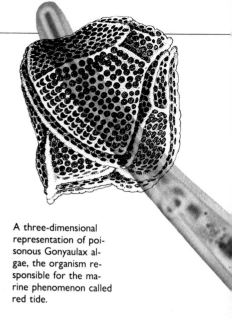

A three-dimensional representation of poisonous Gonyaulax algae, the organism responsible for the marine phenomenon called red tide.

play a vital symbiotic role in the global ecosystem.

Algae and Pollution

While serving a necessary environmental function in most ecosystems, algae can cause disastrous pollution when they overpopulate a particular body of water. This overpopulation occurs when an excessive amount of wastes (most frequently chemical fertilizers, insecticides, herbicides, and chemical wastes from in-

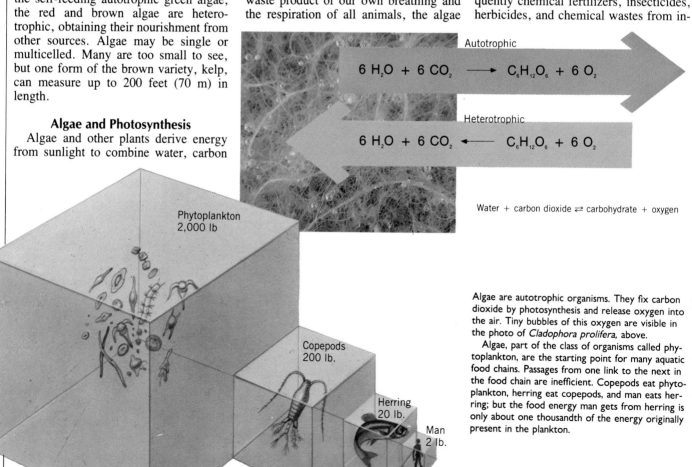

Autotrophic

$$6\ H_2O + 6\ CO_2 \longrightarrow C_6H_{12}O_6 + 6\ O_2$$

Heterotrophic

$$6\ H_2O + 6\ CO_2 \longleftarrow C_6H_{12}O_6 + 6\ O_2$$

Water + carbon dioxide $\rightleftarrows$ carbohydrate + oxygen

Phytoplankton
2,000 lb

Copepods
200 lb.

Herring
20 lb.

Man
2 lb.

Algae are autotrophic organisms. They fix carbon dioxide by photosynthesis and release oxygen into the air. Tiny bubbles of this oxygen are visible in the photo of *Cladophora prolifera*, above.

Algae, part of the class of organisms called phytoplankton, are the starting point for many aquatic food chains. Passages from one link to the next in the food chain are inefficient. Copepods eat phytoplankton, herring eat copepods, and man eats herring; but the food energy man gets from herring is only about one thousandth of the energy originally present in the plankton.

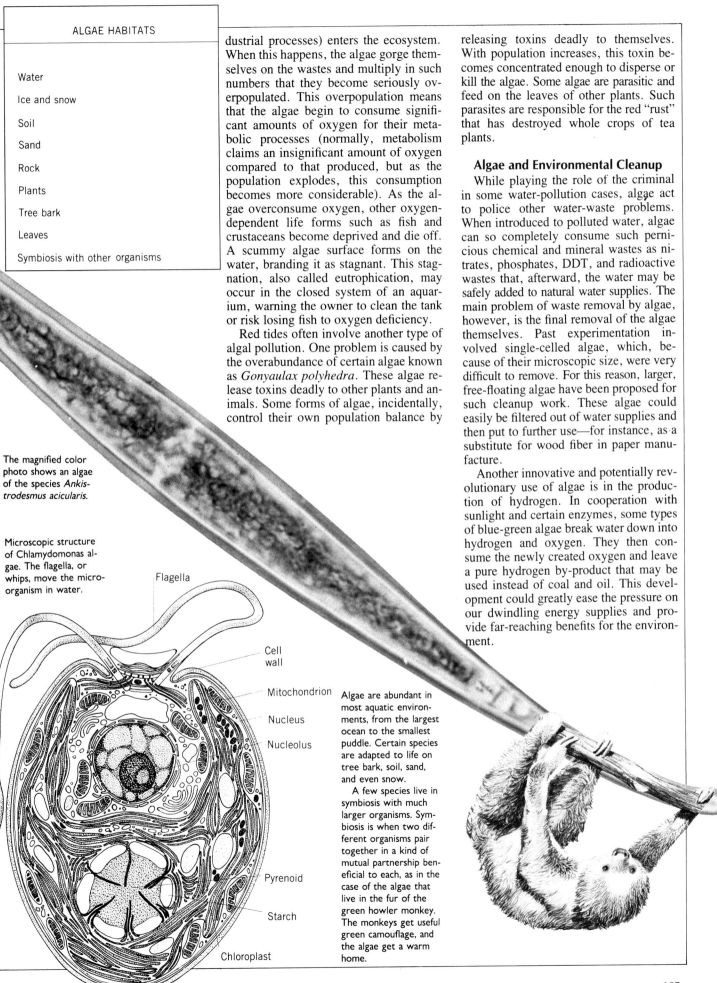

ALGAE HABITATS

Water

Ice and snow

Soil

Sand

Rock

Plants

Tree bark

Leaves

Symbiosis with other organisms

dustrial processes) enters the ecosystem. When this happens, the algae gorge themselves on the wastes and multiply in such numbers that they become seriously overpopulated. This overpopulation means that the algae begin to consume significant amounts of oxygen for their metabolic processes (normally, metabolism claims an insignificant amount of oxygen compared to that produced, but as the population explodes, this consumption becomes more considerable). As the algae overconsume oxygen, other oxygen-dependent life forms such as fish and crustaceans become deprived and die off. A scummy algae surface forms on the water, branding it as stagnant. This stagnation, also called eutrophication, may occur in the closed system of an aquarium, warning the owner to clean the tank or risk losing fish to oxygen deficiency.

Red tides often involve another type of algal pollution. One problem is caused by the overabundance of certain algae known as *Gonyaulax polyhedra*. These algae release toxins deadly to other plants and animals. Some forms of algae, incidentally, control their own population balance by

releasing toxins deadly to themselves. With population increases, this toxin becomes concentrated enough to disperse or kill the algae. Some algae are parasitic and feed on the leaves of other plants. Such parasites are responsible for the red "rust" that has destroyed whole crops of tea plants.

Algae and Environmental Cleanup

While playing the role of the criminal in some water-pollution cases, algae act to police other water-waste problems. When introduced to polluted water, algae can so completely consume such pernicious chemical and mineral wastes as nitrates, phosphates, DDT, and radioactive wastes that, afterward, the water may be safely added to natural water supplies. The main problem of waste removal by algae, however, is the final removal of the algae themselves. Past experimentation involved single-celled algae, which, because of their microscopic size, were very difficult to remove. For this reason, larger, free-floating algae have been proposed for such cleanup work. These algae could easily be filtered out of water supplies and then put to further use—for instance, as a substitute for wood fiber in paper manufacture.

Another innovative and potentially revolutionary use of algae is in the production of hydrogen. In cooperation with sunlight and certain enzymes, some types of blue-green algae break water down into hydrogen and oxygen. They then consume the newly created oxygen and leave a pure hydrogen by-product that may be used instead of coal and oil. This development could greatly ease the pressure on our dwindling energy supplies and provide far-reaching benefits for the environment.

The magnified color photo shows an algae of the species *Ankistrodesmus acicularis*.

Microscopic structure of Chlamydomonas algae. The flagella, or whips, move the microorganism in water.

Flagella

Cell wall

Mitochondrion

Nucleus

Nucleolus

Pyrenoid

Starch

Chloroplast

Algae are abundant in most aquatic environments, from the largest ocean to the smallest puddle. Certain species are adapted to life on tree bark, soil, sand, and even snow.

A few species live in symbiosis with much larger organisms. Symbiosis is when two different organisms pair together in a kind of mutual partnership beneficial to each, as in the case of the algae that live in the fur of the green howler monkey. The monkeys get useful green camouflage, and the algae get a warm home.

Algae as Food and Manufacturing Ingredients

Algae have been used as food in Asia throughout history. About 40 seaweeds are used as foods worldwide, most of them in Japan. Although the human digestive system is unable to break down their complex chemical compounds, seaweeds provide a limited amount of protein and a number of vitamins. Seaweeds are most

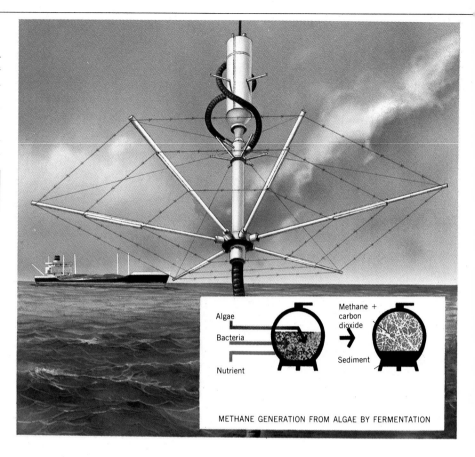

METHANE GENERATION FROM ALGAE BY FERMENTATION

USES OF ALGAE

Human and animal nutrition

Medicines and food additives

Source of bromine and iodine

Production of antibiotics, fertilizers, and methane

Research and scientific applications

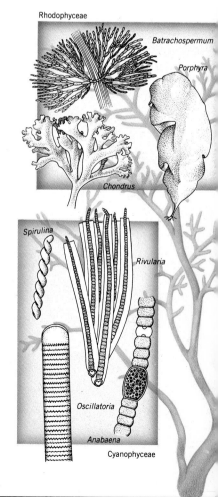

Above: Prototype system developed in the United States for cultivating *Macrocystis pyrifera,* giant algae that grow in strands up to 165 feet (50 m) long. The umbrella-shaped wire frame, normally submerged, supports the algae, which feed on nutrient-rich water pumped from the ocean floor.

Left: Algae farming for human consumption in Japan.

---

valued for their mineral salts, believed to reduce the incidence of goiter, a disease caused by iodine deficiency. Algae have also contributed indirectly to the human diet as a basic ingredient of animal feed and as an organic fertilizer (far preferable to the chemical salt fertilizers blamed in a great many cases of water eutrophication).

Algae also produce gelose, the basic ingredient of gelatin, which is used in foods such as tapioca pudding and aspic. Agar, a gelose-based compound, has an important role in science as an environment for chemical and biological experimentation with microorganisms. Algae

derivatives are also used in a wide range of manufactured commercial products. Some are spun into thread, some are used in plastics, and others figure in a long list of synthetic goods, including car polish, paint, cosmetics, pharmaceuticals, films, and materials such as linoleum and imitation leather. In fossil form, algae are used in various industries, including the production of lime, oil and dynamite production.

Whether considered in their present, past, or future capacities, algae are worldwide participants in a great number of different processes that constitute life on Earth.

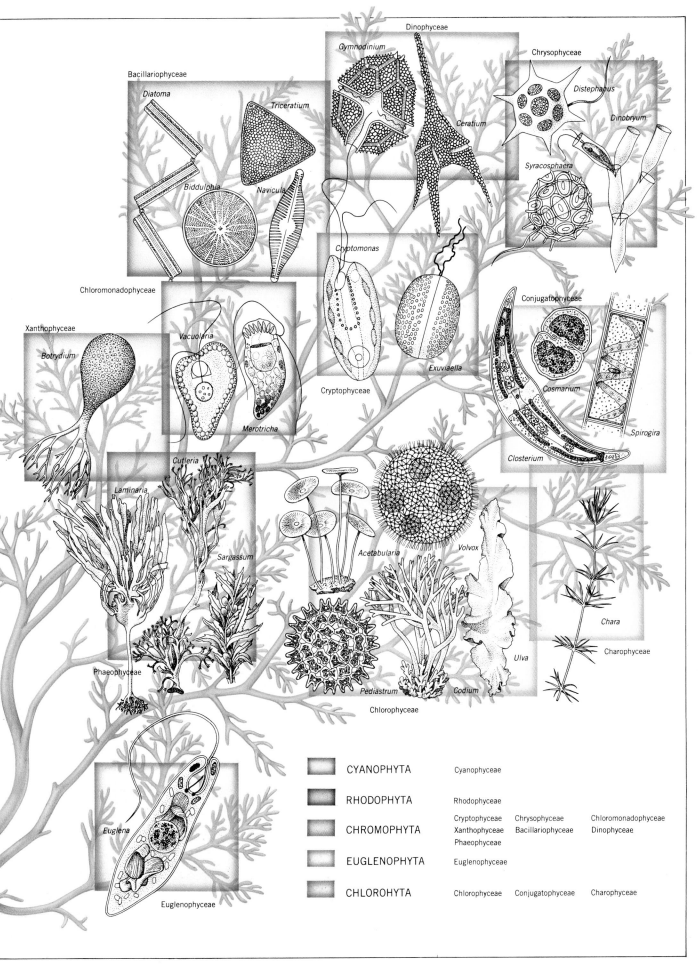

Dinophyceae

Bacillariophyceae

Chrysophyceae

Diatoma

Gymnodinium

Triceratium

Distephanus

Ceratium

Dinobryum

Biddulphia

Navicula

Syracosphaera

Chloromonadophyceae

Cryptomonas

Conjugatophyceae

Xanthophyceae

Vacuolaria

Botrydium

Cosmarium

Exuviaella

Merotricha

Cryptophyceae

Spirogira

Closterium

Cutleria

Laminaria

Acetabularia

Volvox

Sargassum

Chara

Ulva

Charophyceae

Phaeophyceae

Pediastrum

Codium

Chlorophyceae

	CYANOPHYTA	Cyanophyceae		
	RHODOPHYTA	Rhodophyceae		
	CHROMOPHYTA	Cryptophyceae	Chrysophyceae	Chloromonadophyceae
		Xanthophyceae	Bacillariophyceae	Dinophyceae
		Phaeophyceae		
	EUGLENOPHYTA	Euglenophyceae		
	CHLOROHYTA	Chlorophyceae	Conjugatophyceae	Charophyceae

Euglena

Euglenophyceae

109

Alkaline Earth Metals

Several hundred years ago, chemists referred to solid substances that appeared to be relatively inert as earths. These earths were not metals, would not dissolve in water (or only slightly), and were unaffected by high temperatures. Certain members of the group of these so-called earths were found to be alkaline—that is, they tended to neutralize acids—and were therefore called alkaline earths. They included the substances then known as magnesia, strontia, baryta, and lime.

By the beginning of the 19th century, chemists discovered that the alkaline earths were not in fact elements but compounds. They were found to be compounds of a hitherto unknown group of metals with oxygen. This new group of metals inherited the designation alkaline earths, and some of them were named after the earths from which they were extracted, including magnesium (from magnesia), strontium (strontia), and barium (baryta). Calcium, another alkaline earth metal, was named after the Latin word for lime, while beryllium was named for beryl, the mineral from which it was first extracted. Radium, discovered by Pierre and Marie Curie, was named for its radioactivity.

Chemical Families

A family of elements, such as the alkaline earth family, is a group whose members all exhibit similar chemical properties. From a physical standpoint, the alkaline earth metals resemble each other somewhat; they are mostly silver-white metals (although beryllium is gray) that tarnish easily. But it is because of the similarities in their chemical properties that they are placed in the same family.

The periodic table is a chart of all the elements according to their atomic structure. On this chart, elements of the same family are found in the same column. In the column to the extreme left is the family of elements known as the alkali metals. The alkaline earth metals are those in the second column from the left.

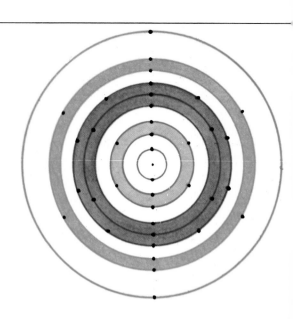

The alkaline earth metals (represented here by beryllium, the lightest of the group) have an outer shell of two electrons that are readily released to halogens or oxygen. They form ion bonds with a valence of +2.

Despite the fact that they were once classified as earths, they are not at all inert. Several ignite spontaneously with air when ground into fine powder. And they are so chemically active that none is found in the pure state in nature.

Chemical Activity

The chemical activity of an element depends upon the structure of its atoms; specifically, upon how the electrons are arranged about the nucleus. These electrons may be thought of as grouped in a small number of restricted groups called shells, with each shell able to contain only a certain maximum number of electrons. If the outer shell of an atom is fully occupied, the atom is chemically inactive. If, on the other hand, an atom has an unfilled outer shell, it may bond with an atom of another element by sharing the electrons with that atom or by transferring its outer-shell electrons to the atom.

The alkaline earths are less reactive than the alkali metals because it is harder for an atom to release two electrons than it is to give up only one (as is the case with the alkali metals).

Alkaline Earths in Industry and Nature

All of the alkaline earths are used commercially in one form or another, particularly beryllium, magnesium, and calcium. Beryllium, the lightest of the alkaline earths, is occasionally used for certain purposes where light weight is essential, as in nuclear weapons. Magnesium is a commonly used structural material. One-third lighter than aluminum, it is the second most inexpensive metal, next to iron. Its light weight and strength make it ideal for use in aircraft and missiles—there is thought to be more magnesium in orbit than any other metal. Calcium is a component of limestone, which, in turn, is a component of cement.

Many of the alkaline earths are essential for life. Some scientists think that this may be related to the fact that life evolved from the sea, where there are relatively high concentrations of alkaline earth ions. Magnesium, for instance, is present in chlorophyll, while calcium is an important ingredient of leaves, bones, and shells.

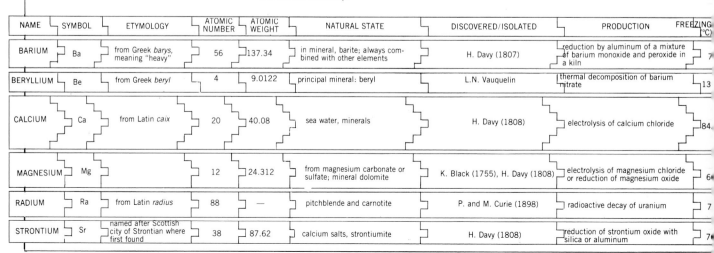

NAME	SYMBOL	ETYMOLOGY	ATOMIC NUMBER	ATOMIC WEIGHT	NATURAL STATE	DISCOVERED/ISOLATED	PRODUCTION	FREEZING (°C)
BARIUM	Ba	from Greek *barys*, meaning "heavy"	56	137.34	in mineral, barite; always combined with other elements	H. Davy (1807)	reduction by aluminum of a mixture of barium monoxide and peroxide in a kiln	7
BERYLLIUM	Be	from Greek *beryl*	4	9.0122	principal mineral: beryl	L.N. Vauquelin	thermal decomposition of barium nitrate	13
CALCIUM	Ca	from Latin *caix*	20	40.08	sea water, minerals	H. Davy (1808)	electrolysis of calcium chloride	84
MAGNESIUM	Mg		12	24.312	from magnesium carbonate or sulfate; mineral dolomite	K. Black (1755), H. Davy (1808)	electrolysis of magnesium chloride or reduction of magnesium oxide	6
RADIUM	Ra	from Latin *radius*	88	—	pitchblende and carnotite	P. and M. Curie (1898)	radioactive decay of uranium	7
STRONTIUM	Sr	named after Scottish city of Strontian where first found	38	87.62	calcium salts, strontiumite	H. Davy (1808)	reduction of strontium oxide with silica or aluminum	7

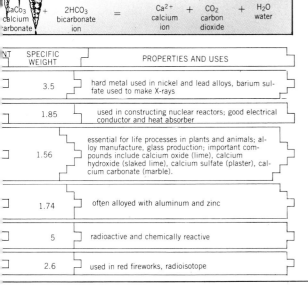

Comparative Sizes of Atoms and Ions of Alkaline Earth Metals

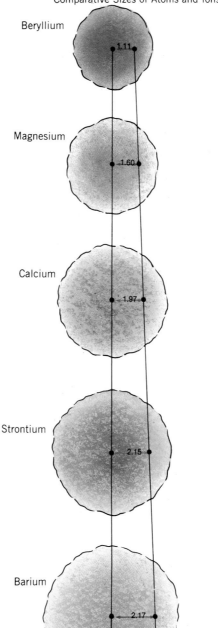

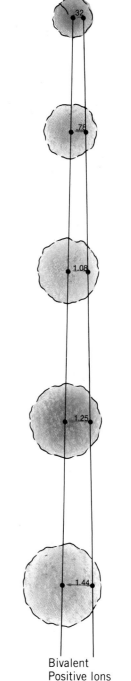

Stalactite formation

Dissolved calcium carbonate re-
forms in stalactites giving off
carbon dioxide and water vapor

$$CaCo_3 + 2HCO_3 = Ca^{2+} + CO_2 + H_2O$$

calcium   bicarbonate   calcium   carbon   water
carbonate   ion   ion   dioxide

NT	SPECIFIC WEIGHT	PROPERTIES AND USES
☐	3.5	hard metal used in nickel and lead alloys, barium sulfate used to make X-rays
☐	1.85	used in constructing nuclear reactors; good electrical conductor and heat absorber
☐	1.56	essential for life processes in plants and animals; alloy manufacture, glass production; important compounds include calcium oxide (lime), calcium hydroxide (slaked lime), calcium sulfate (plaster), calcium carbonate (marble).
☐	1.74	often alloyed with aluminum and zinc
☐	5	radioactive and chemically reactive
☐	2.6	used in red fireworks, radioisotope

Beryllium   1.11   .32

Magnesium   1.60   .78

Calcium   1.97   1.08

Strontium   2.15   1.25

Barium   2.17   1.44

Atoms

Bivalent
Positive Ions

111

Alkaloid

Long before the beginning of recorded history, people must surely have been experimenting with the material they found in the world around them. The plant kingdom would have offered the greatest riches, and by trial and error people must have learned that some plants give nourishment and some do not. Many that could not be used for food could serve other functions. A large group of these plants—possibly 10 to 15 percent of all species—was found to contain certain chemical compounds that we know today as alkaloids. The ancients were familiar with many of these substances, but it was not until early in the development of modern chemistry, in the 19th century, that they began to be classed together and were given the collective name of alkaloids. The name itself could not have been given to them much sooner than it was because it indicates that they were all recognized as being alkaline—that is, they tend to neutralize acids—and the nature of the relationship between acids and bases, or alkaline substances, did not begin to become clear until the early 1800s.

The most important characteristic of alkaloids is that many of them have medicinal, pharmacological, and psychoactive properties. These cover a wide range of effects, from poisons such as strychnine and ergot, to medicines such as quinine and ephedrine, to narcotics such as morphine and codeine, and to psychedelics such as mescaline and psilocybin. Veterinarians eventually came to understand their effects on livestock, which were sometimes disastrous. During the Middle Ages, there was a singular case of mass poisoning of livestock and people by ergot (a fungus that grows on cereal grains and contains natural lysergic acid, a chemical compound related to LSD). Modern studies indicate that some outbreaks of mass hysteria in the Middle Ages were due to the effect of this component of the fungus. Alkaloids are also of vital social significance because of their frequent abuse as narcotics and hallucinogens.

Medical Uses

On the positive side, alkaloids have many medicinal applications—some of them of dramatic interest, as in the case of ergonovine, an ergot derivative widely used in obstetrics to constrict blood vessels and thus reduce the danger of hemorrhage after childbirth.

In the following listing of the chief applications of alkaloids, you will note the names of some of our commonest and most reliable drugs.

Analgesics (pain-killers). The most effective natural drug ever found for the suppression of pain is morphine, an alkaloid isolated from opium, which in turn is

ALKALOID	PRINCIPAL SOURCE	FAMILY	CHARACTERISTICS AND USES
Atropine	*Atropa belladonna* (belladonna)	Solanaceae	Dilates pupils, paralyzes nerve endings, antidote for fungi poisoning
Caffeine	*Coffea arabica* (coffee)	Rubiaceae	Cardiac stimulant, diuretic
	Thea sinensis (tea)	Teaceae	
	Ilex paraguariensis (yerba maté)	Aquifoliaceae	
	Theobroma cacao (coco)	Sterculiaceae	
	Cola acuminata (cola)	Sterculiaceae	
Quinine	*Cinchona ledgeriana*	Rubiaceae	Used to treat malaria
Cocaine	*Erthroxylon coca* (coco)	Eritrossilaceae	Paralyzes peripheral nervous system, dilates pupils, increases body temperature
Codeine	*Papever somniferum* (poppies)	Papaveraceae	Narcotic similar to morphine
Curare	*Strychnos toxifera*	Loganiaceae	Extremely poisonous muscle relaxant
Morphine	*Papaver somniferum*	Papaveraceae	Narcotic that acts on central nervous system
Nicotine	*Nicotiana rustica* (tobacco)	Solanaceae	Used in preparation of insecticides and nicotinic acids
	Nicotiana tabacum (tobacco)		
Opium	*Papaver somniferum*	Papaveraceae	Mixture of 25 alkaloids made from juice of unripe poppy capsules
Strychnine	*Strychnos nux-vomica*	Loganiaceae	Strong poison, used in small quantities as a neuro-stimulant

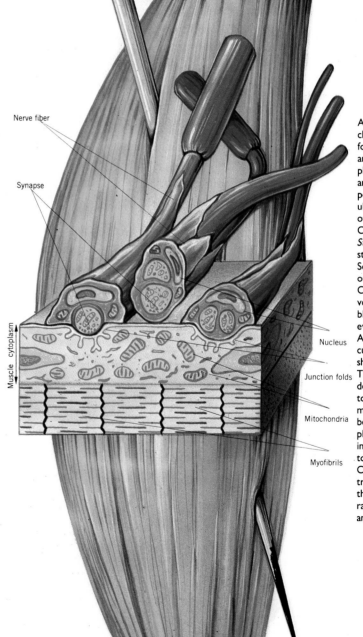

Nerve fiber

Synapse

Muscle cytoplasm

Nucleus

Junction folds

Mitochondria

Myofibrils

Alkaloids are a class of chemical compounds found mainly in plants and known for their physiological effects on animals. They include poisons, narcotics, stimulants, anesthetics, and other medicinal agents. Curare, an extract of *Strychnos toxifera*, is still used today by South American Indians on hunting arrow tips. Curare paralyzes the voluntary muscles, blocks respiration, and eventually causes death. A muscle pierced by a curare-tipped arrow is shown in the diagram. The enlargement shows details of a muscle motor unit, consisting of muscle fibers, nerve fibers, and motor end plates that transmit the impulse for contraction to the muscle fiber. Curare blocks this transmission, paralyzing the muscle and temporarily immobilizing the animal.

derived from the juice of the young opium poppy. In spite of its addictive properties, it is still very widely used. Two other derivatives of opium are codeine and heroin. The latter was first developed and marketed as an even more powerful analgesic that, it was hoped, might double as a cure for morphine addiction. Unfortunately, it turned out that heroin is even more addictive than morphine. Today, heroin is banned even for medical use in most countries.

Heart stimulants. Alkaloids from the bark of a tree, cinchona, particularly quinidine, are used to correct irregular heart rhythm. Compounds made from tropical trees of the genus Rauwolfia are used to lower blood pressure in cases of hypertension.

Respiratory stimulants. These include coniine, cytisine, lobeline, and the familiar nicotine, obtained from tobacco. Some are highly dangerous drugs, since their effect is often followed by an opposite reaction, and the patient can easily die from respiratory arrest or convulsions.

Blood vessel constrictors. The best known are ergonovine, mentioned above, and ephedrine, used to counteract the effects of colds, sinusitis, hay fever, and bronchial asthma. Ephedrine is useful in restoring blood pressure to normal in shock (hypotension).

Pupil dilators (used in eye examinations and eye surgery). These include ephedrine, atropine, scopolamine, and cocaine.

Local anesthetics. The most familiar is cocaine, but its undesirable side effects have led to a great effort to develop synthetic substitutes. Several such substances have been developed, but cocaine is still used occasionally in medicine.

Muscle relaxants. The best known is curare, originally used as an arrow poison by South American Indians.

Malaria treatment. Until recently, the only really effective treatment for malaria was alkaloids derived from cinchona, especially quinine.

Chemistry

Not only the desire for greater scientific understanding, but also the hope of improving the human condition by developing more effective drugs, led chemists to intensive study of the composition of alkaloids. Opium, a drug known to the ancients, was the first alkaloid source so studied. The first two alkaloids isolated (probably narcotine and morphine) were described in 1803 and 1804. But the first synthesis—that is, artificial creation in a laboratory—of an alkaloid did not occur until 1886, with coniine, which had been first isolated from hemlock nearly 60 years earlier.

Synthesis is important for several reasons. In some cases, it is the only way to test the accuracy of analysis. In others, it is the first step toward designing new and slightly modified versions of existing alkaloids to obtain a drug without certain side effects. Much work has been done since the 19th century to isolate, analyze, and synthesize alkaloids. But it has not always been easy. For example, a synthetic form of the alkaloid strychnine was produced only after many years of research.

The main constituents of alkaloids are nitrogen, carbon, and hydrogen. Although the more than 2,000 known varieties of alkaloids all have somewhat different molecules, there is one characteristic that most have in common. The carbon atoms are usually in a ring structure, or cyclic system. That is, usually five, but sometimes four carbon atoms are joined in a circle to one nitrogen atom and to each other by single or double bonds, with enough hydrogen atoms to satisfy valence requirements.

What this means can best be understood by trying to visualize this basic component of alkaloid molecules in the same way that chemists do. A molecule with five carbon atoms and one of nitrogen can be represented as a hexagon in this way,

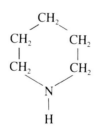

with all the atoms occupying the positions shown in the diagram. This shows a single atom of nitrogen bonded to a single hydrogen atom and to two carbon atoms that are part of the ring. Each of these carbon atoms is bonded in turn to two hydrogen atoms as well as to another carbon atom. The diagram

is used to represent the same thing. Using the same principle, a molecule with four carbon atoms and one of nitrogen is shown as

Each connection, or bond, means that a pair of electrons is shared by two atoms; sometimes, however, two pairs of electrons are shared by a pair of atoms, and the excess hydrogen atoms are simply dropped from the molecule. This can be represented as

or even as

The first of these two diagrams shows that the nitrogen atom has formed a double bond on one side and a single one on the other, and so it releases one hydrogen atom. Each carbon atom also forms a double bond on one side and a single bond on the other. This leaves it able to hold on to only one hydrogen atom. The structure of nicotine contains all the elements discussed above. This can be shown either as

or, with everything spelled out, as

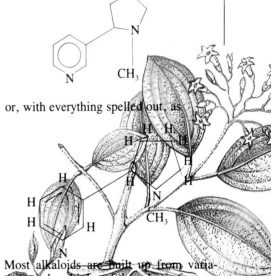

Most alkaloids are built up from variations and multiples of these basic forms.

Still mysterious is the function of alkaloids in the plants that produce them. Two things we do know are that their presence often protects some plants from some—but not all—insects and that they are found in much larger amounts before seed formation than after. They are also found in widely varying amounts in plants of the same family. And the fact that they are not produced at all by some 85 to 90 percent of all plants throws the question of their usefulness to the plants in doubt.
See ACIDS AND BASES; CHEMICAL BOND AND VALENCE; CHEMISTRY.

115

Allergy

Although it has been known for hundreds of years that some things we eat, drink, breathe, or touch cause peculiar reactions in some of us, these abnormal reactions called allergies are just now yielding their secrets to medical science.

All of the cells in our bodies are coded according to our own particular genetic makeup. This allows millions of different cells to perform their own special tasks without interfering with each other. The cells of our body can also tolerate a wide variety of cells other than our own *as if* they came under our own codes—in other words, failing to recognize that they don't belong. But in some circumstances, our bodies refuse to grant this "visa" to foreign cells, and our immune system attacks them as invaders. This essential defense against harmful substances such as infectious bacteria and viruses is necessary for life. In an allergic reaction, however, the immune system overreacts to foreign cells or attacks ordinary substances, such as pollen, that most people tolerate.

Symptoms

Allergic reactions may vary in severity from minor irritation of the skin to total disability and, in some cases, death. Common reactions include itching, burning, and tingling sensations; skin rashes, hives, welts, and swelling; watering and smarting of the eyes; breathing difficulties, lung congestion (accumulation of fluid), and cough; nausea, vomiting, and diarrhea; weakness, muscle soreness, and spasms; depression, drowsiness, inability to concentrate, anxiety, migraine, and convulsions; and urinary-tract burning and vaginal itch.

Sensitization and Atopy

There are two basic categories of allergy: sensitization and atopy. A German physician, Clemens von Pirquet, described sensitization in 1906 when he observed a physical reaction in individuals after repeated exposure to certain substances. Earlier, in 1873, a British doctor named Charles Harrison Blackley had noted that grass pollen can almost instantaneously cause hay fever in some people.

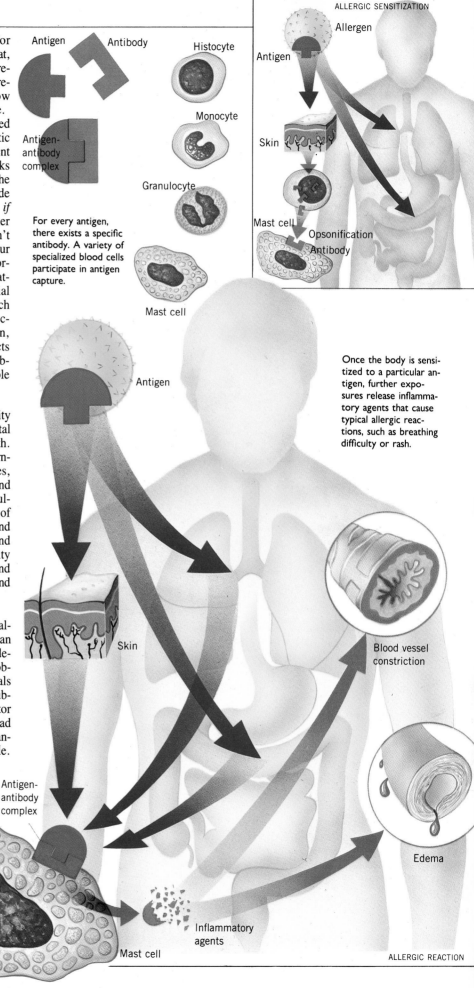

For every antigen, there exists a specific antibody. A variety of specialized blood cells participate in antigen capture.

Once the body is sensitized to a particular antigen, further exposures release inflammatory agents that cause typical allergic reactions, such as breathing difficulty or rash.

Allergens can enter the body through three areas—the skin, the respiratory system, or the gastrointestinal tract. Once in the body, they trigger the production of the antibody specific to the antigen they carry. These antibodies attach themselves to the mast cells.

ALLERGIC SENSITIZATION

Allergen
Antigen
Skin
Mast cell
Opsonification
Antibody

Antigen
Antibody
Histocyte
Monocyte
Granulocyte
Mast cell

Antigen-antibody complex

Antigen

Skin

Antigen-antibody complex

Blood vessel constriction

Edema

Inflammatory agents

Mast cell

ALLERGIC REACTION

He studied the reaction of such allergy sufferers by applying pollen on the inner lining of their eyes or scratching it onto their skin. He noted that it caused a certain kind of inflammation that was distinct from the reaction of nonallergic persons. Now called atopy, this inflammation is different from sensitization in that it is a spontaneous reaction (not requiring previous exposure). Hay fever is one of many hereditary allergies—it runs in families.

Antigens and Antibodies

The substance that triggers the allergic reaction is variously called the allergen, antigen, or more recently, the immunogen. When it comes into contact with certain body tissues, they release a substance called antibody, which combines with the antigen and destroys it with the help of other body defenses. (Every antigen is fought by one specific type of antibody, which has a shape that enables it to attach to the antigen's surface.) This same antibody defense system is used to fight off bacteria and other foreign agents, except that in an allergic reaction, some additional substances are produced, including histamine. When histamine is released into the body tissue, it becomes an irritant and

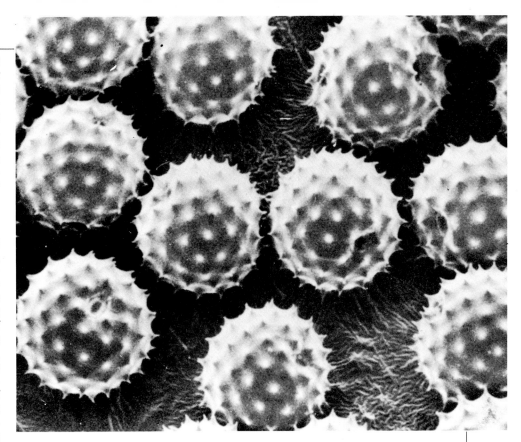

is responsible for some of the symptoms of the allergy, including inflammation, pain, and swelling.

Allergies may be acute or chronic. There are many substances to which a significant number of people are allergic. Among the common foods suspected of causing low-level chronic allergic reactions are sugar, coffee, and chocolate.

The first clue to how allergic reactions take place also helped doctors understand the allergen-antibody mechanism. In the early 1920s, a German physician named Otto Prausnitz injected himself with the blood serum (or fluid portion of the blood containing no cells) of his colleague Heinz Küstner, who had a fish allergy. Several days later, Prausnitz ate fish and became ill. This led to the development of the passive transfer (P-T) test, still commonly used for diagnosis today. This test consists of injecting a small amount of serum from an allergic patient just under the skin of a normal subject and later injecting allergens at the same site. The offending allergen produces a hive.

Allergy Treatment Categories

Allergies are treated by medical professionals called allergists. They classify allergic reactions into four major categories. These differ on the basis of the kinds of allergens involved, the mechanisms by which the body reacts to them, and the kind of reaction observed in the sufferer.

Atopic reactions involve the immediate release of histamine. They may be caused by a bee sting or by common allergens to which a person has become oversusceptible. Atopic reactions include anaphylaxes (a severe, acute body reaction characterized by breathing difficulty), itching and burning of the skin (urticaria), shock, and occasionally diarrhea and vomiting. Anaphylactic shock is potentially fatal and is treated with the injection of a strong stimulant, epinephrin (adrenalin). Milder atopic reactions in this category include hay fever and food allergies typically causing itchy skin or welts and a burning sensation. These symptoms usually disappear by themselves.

Another category of allergy involves changes in the blood serum and includes the severe reactions associated with incompatible blood transfusions (blood type unmatched) or with acute penicillin reactions.

Special kinds of immune-related diseases such as rheumatoid arthritis (a painful condition of the joints) and viral hepatitis (a viral liver disease) constitute another category of allergies in which the body harms its own tissues.

Delayed reactions such as contact dermatitis (skin irritation caused by something with which you come in contact) are another type of allergy. Poison ivy, oak, or sumac produce this type of reaction.

Certain kinds of employment may also carry a risk of allergy. Wheat allergy is common among bakers, whereas allergies to dyes and other chemicals are common in industry. Some food additives are also known to produce an allergic reaction.

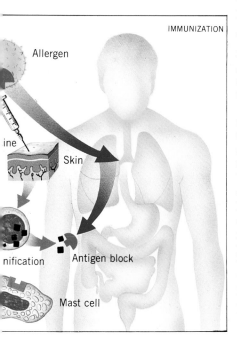

IMMUNIZATION

Allergen

ine

Skin

nification

Antigen block

Mast cell

In some cases, it is possible to create an immunity to a given allergen by exposing the body to low doses of the material over a long period of time. It has been theorized that human populations adapt themselves to local allergen environments in this way through constant exposure to allergy agents in air, drinking water, and locally grown food.

Alloy

Practically wherever we look, we find metals. Yet in very few cases do we encounter pure metals. Instead, almost all the metallic substances we find—in nature as well as in man-made products—are combinations of a metal with other substances, most often other metals. These combinations of a metal with other substances are called alloys.

Base Metal and Alloying Agents

In most cases, alloys consist primarily of a given metal, called the base, to which is added a small amount of other materials, called the alloying agents. For example, steel—perhaps the most common alloy—is mostly iron, plus 1.5 percent or less carbon, measured by weight. Carbon is fairly unique in being one of the few nonmetallic alloying agents. Alloys with more than two or three alloying agents, and whose alloying agents constitute more than a few percent of their weight, are not common and are said to be highly alloyed. Base metal and alloying agents are usually combined while they are molten (fluid). However, sometimes alloys are made by fusing together a mixture of powders of the various materials.

Why Make Alloys?

By combining metals into alloys, we are able to create materials that have

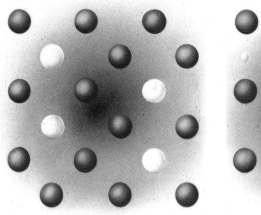

The formation of alloys depends upon the capability of metal atoms to form crystalline structures. *Above:* At left, atoms entering a crystal structure are replacing those previously there; at right, atoms are entering spaces of the crystal lattice.

In the diagrams at right, regular substitution has produced a multiphase crystal alloy.

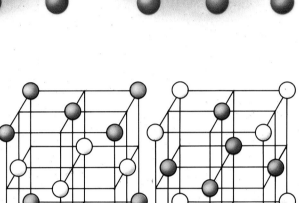

properties suited to particular—and often very demanding—uses. For example, plugs in fire-protection sprinkler systems must have a low melting point. Lead is the base of an alloy with cadmium, tin, and bismuth that can be used for this purpose. Other alloys increase the strength or raise the resistance to corrosion and high temperature of a base metal. A whole family of strong but light alloys is made with metals like aluminum and titanium. These alloys are important for making aircraft. Scientists are constantly working on new alloys, designed to meet an incredible variety of specifications.

The Microstructure of Alloys

Solid metals are composed of crystals—atoms arranged in symmetrical shapes, such as cubes. At different temperatures, the crystal structure of metals can change; in fact, in molten metals, atoms flow freely without an ordered structure. Different structures of atoms are called phases. When metals are mixed together, the resulting alloy can be single-phase or multiphase. Single-phase alloys have one predominating crystal structure—usually that of the base metal. The atoms of the alloying agents can, with a random distribution, substitute in the crystal structure for atoms of the base

SOME IMPORTANT ALLOYS					
IRON ALLOYS	Percent of Iron	Percent of Carbon	Characteristics	Applications	
Carbon steel	no more than 99.8	no more than .2	malleable	car bodies	
Steel	99.8–98	.2–2	hard	machine parts	
Cast iron	97–94	3–6	hard, brittle	heavy castings	
COPPER ALLOYS	Percent of copper	Percent of zinc	Percent of tin	Characteristics	Applications
Brass	90	10	—	beautiful	costume jewelry
Brass-72	72	28	—	color, ductile	stamped parts
				and malleable	
Bronze	82	6	12		

LIGHT ALLOYS

Heat-treatable aluminum alloys	Varying percentages of aluminum, magnesium, copper, silicon Characteristics: high corrosion resistance, workable in hot or cold state Applications: aeronautical industry
Non-heat-treatable aluminum alloys	Aluminum, silicon, magnesium, manganese, iron Characteristics: good corrosion resistance Applications: chemical industry, marine environments
Titanium alloys	Varying percentages of titanium, aluminum, tin Characteristics: high resistance to heat Applications: aeronautical industry

OTHER ALLOYS

Nickel-chromium	50% nickel, 30% iron, 20% chromium Characteristics: high corrosion resistance Applications: ships, chemical industry
White Gold	80% gold, 10% nickel, 5% copper, 5% zinc Applications: used in jewelry
Pewter	91% tin, 6% antimony, 1.5% copper, 1.5% lead Applications: used for tea and coffee services and decorative objects
Alpha Brass	60% copper, 20% zinc, 20% nickel Characteristics: low friction production, low melting point Applications: precision instruments
Alloy steel	16% chromium, 8% nickel, varying percentages of iron and carbon Characteristics: hardness, toughness, corrosion resistance Applications: precision instruments

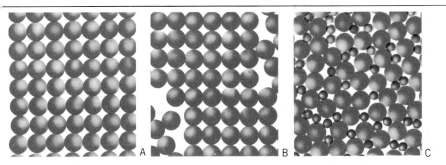

Diagram A shows the crystal lattice of a metal; if the structure is heated to a high temperature, spaces form in the structure; in B, these spaces remain if the metal is cooled quickly, but the metal becomes harder and more rigid. The same may occur when other substances are added to the crystal lattice changing the structure, as in C.

ALLOY RESISTANCE

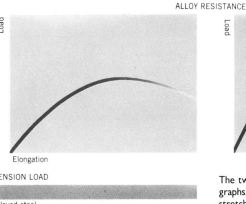

Load

Elongation

Load

Elasticity limit

Elongation

TENSION LOAD

Alloyed steel

Steel with a high carbon content

Nickel alloy

Carbon steel

Aluminum alloy

Brass

Copper

Silver

The two charts above are tension-elongation graphs. All metals subjected to a certain load will stretch. The first graph shows the stretching of a material with a given elasticity. When the load is removed, the material returns to its original shape. In the second graph, the material also stretches as the load increases, but then it reaches the elasticity limit and the material yields more readily. If the load is removed, the material does not return to its original shape. As a material's elasticity limit increases, so does its suitability for use in construction.

Left: Bar graph depicts the elasticity limit of several metals and metal alloys.

metal. Or, if the alloying atoms are sufficiently smaller than the base atoms, the former can fit in between the latter. In both cases, the alloy is called a solid solution, because the alloying metal has been dissolved into the base metal.

In multiphase alloys, two or more crystal structures are intermingled among each other. That is, instead of all the atoms of one metal fitting into the crystals of another, separate crystal structures, composed of atoms of one or more of the given metals, come into intimate contact without breaking down. Multiphase alloys are far more common than single-phase alloys, and their microstructures can be extremely complex.

The various properties of alloys originate in both their constituents and their microstructures. For example, stainless steel is made resistant to corrosion primarily by the presence of chromium, which does not deteriorate as easily as iron in certain environments. Added strength results from changes in a metal's crystal structure. When a metal is bent, for instance, a deformation occurs in its crystal structure; some crystals are moved or distorted. In the pure metal, such deformations might take place in well-defined ways. But when the metal is alloyed, the presence of other atoms—or other crystal structures—impedes deformations in the basic crystal structure. Thus, the alloy is stronger than the base metal alone.
See LIGHT ALLOYS.

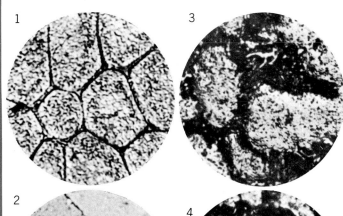

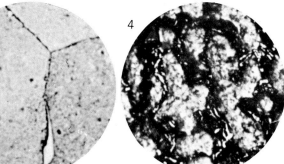

Far left (1 and 2): lead and 2.2% antimony alloys used for bird shot. *Near left:* instead, photographs 3 and 4 show the structural change according to the amount of antimony alloyed with lead; 5% in 3 and 1.8% in 4. These alloys are for plates in lead-acid batteries.

Alternative Medicine

When you go to your doctor—either because you're feeling ill or because it's time for your periodic checkup—the physician, as a matter of course, palpates (examines by feeling) your abdomen. Traditional practitioners in Western countries use this method to look for trouble beneath the abdominal wall (swellings or unusual hardness or softness in the underlying organs). A traditional practitioner in Asia would also examine this wall, but he would be focusing instead on the flow of energy throughout your body. This is indicated by your body's sensitivity to the pressure of his hands in the "meridians," or energy pathways, that meet in the abdominal wall.

Basic Theory

For the last 250 years, Western doctors have been combating disease by identifying the infecting bacterium (the germ) and locating the specific site of the infection. Traditional Eastern doctors emphasize a state of health characterized by a perfect balance of energy within the body. A Western physician makes a diagnosis and then generally prescribes a drug treatment designed to eliminate a harmful microbe. A traditional Oriental physician, after diagnosis, initiates a program of acupuncture, massage, and herbal remedies. This program is designed to regulate the body's energy balance. In traditional Western medicine, a diseased body is frequently described as being besieged by foreign invaders. Eastern medical practitioners believe that a body becomes susceptible to disease when its internal balance is off; consequently, it is the entire patient and his environment that needs treatment.

The concept that symptoms, infections, and chronic pathological conditions should be treated with emphasis on the entire person, rather than on the specific medical problem, is gaining acceptance in Western countries. By no means has it replaced traditional modes of examination and treatment. Increased cultural ex-

In the practice of oriental medicine, acupuncture therapy is based on adjusting the balance within the body of two contrasting but complementary forms of vital energy: *Yin* and *Yang*.

These two fundamental forces, according to Eastern philosophy, govern all life and the existence of the Universe itself. Yang, the masculine principle, is the sky and Sun, light and warmth. The female principle, Yin, is Earth, darkness and cold. In symbolic representations, Yang is white and Yin black or red.

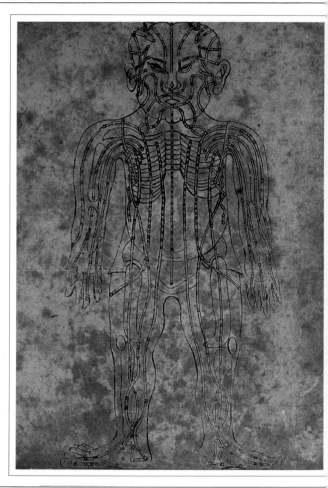

HOMEOPATHY	IRIDOLOGY	ZONAL MASSAGE	CHIROPRACTIC	HYPNOSIS
A system of therapy based on the treatment of illness by administering extremely small quantities of substances that, in larger doses, would provoke the same symptoms the patient exhibits. Thus, fever is treated with an extremely dilute solution of a fever-causing agent, and so on.	A diagnostic technique that considers the iris of the eye (*iridos* in Greek) to be a window on the internal functioning of the body. Illnesses and organic disfunctions are diagnosed by observing the changing color, structure, and density of the iris as it is affected by the state of the various body organs.	It is held that the density of nerve cells in the hands and the feet give them a disproportional influence on the central nervous system and on the functioning of the body in general. Appropriate massage of these sensitive extremities, then, could have a positive effect on the general level of health.	A system of treatment that depends on the manipulation of the skeletal and muscular systems of the body, in particular, the spinal column. Therapy is intended to improve nerve function. A related discipline, osteopathy, uses similar manipulations with the intent of improving blood flow.	Therapeutic uses are principally those of helping patient reestablish control over themselves in some respect—for instance, quit smoking—or bring forward repressed memories in some forms of psychotherapy. Hypnotic anesthesia may used in certain kinds of minsurgery and childbirth.

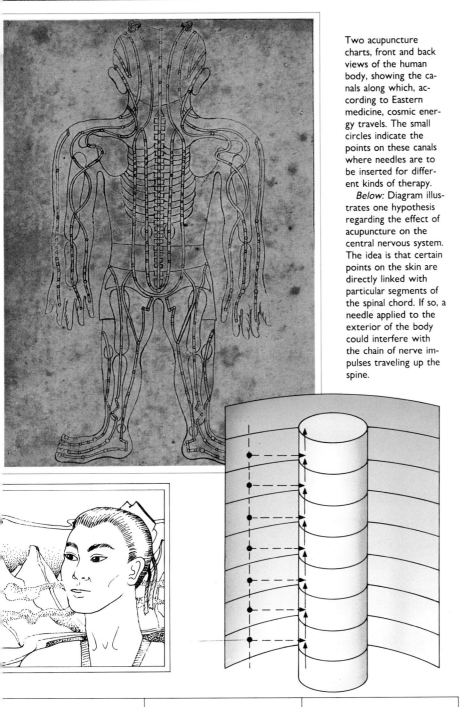

Two acupuncture charts, front and back views of the human body, showing the canals along which, according to Eastern medicine, cosmic energy travels. The small circles indicate the points on these canals where needles are to be inserted for different kinds of therapy.

Below: Diagram illustrates one hypothesis regarding the effect of acupuncture on the central nervous system. The idea is that certain points on the skin are directly linked with particular segments of the spinal chord. If so, a needle applied to the exterior of the body could interfere with the chain of nerve impulses traveling up the spine.

change between East and West has played an important role in this change—though the 19th-century German physician Samuel Hahnemann, who founded the science of homeopathy, also advanced the notion that discrepant energy levels are the root of disease.

Major Modes of Practice

Acupuncture, homeopathy, megavitamin treatments, nutrition, as well as evaluation of a person's emotional and spiritual states are major practical methods in alternative medicine.

Basically, acupuncture consists of inserting needles into the skin in one or more of 365 spots on the body, so as to redirect, intensify, or diminish the energy flow to particular organs. If the practitioner finds abnormal rigidity, coolness, or warmth in your abdominal wall, he may conclude that there is a problem in your liver. By inserting needles in various sites along this meridian—on your big toe, ankle, calf, and thigh, for example—he will modulate the energy flow from, to, and around the liver. Acupuncture is one aspect of alternative medicine that can be evaluated scientifically. There is now considerable evidence that acupuncture can induce physiologic responses in the patient. One theory for the effectiveness of acupuncture in diminishing chronic pain is that the procedure is able to increase the production of the body's natural painkiller—beta endorphin.

A visit to a homeopathist consists, in great part, of your describing your physical and emotional state. He wants to hear about your bothersome, though not necessarily clinically pathological, symptoms, such as fatigue, tension, occasional acne flare-ups. He is also interested in your lifestyle, habits, and physical environment. On the basis of what you have told him and what he has observed, he will prescribe a regimen of primarily herbal remedies and minimum-potency drugs along with a diet, to regulate chemical imbalances .

Megavitamin therapy consists of very large doses of vitamins taken to prevent or cure disease.

Alternative medicine is often called holistic medicine, from the Greek *holos,* "whole." Its emphasis is on the whole person rather than on a specific, isolated pathology. Increasingly, it is being regarded as a valuable complement to traditional and often highly technological modes of medical practice. At the same time, many Western physicians feel that the emphasis on alternative medicine sometimes leads patients to treat themselves more than they should. A reasonable balance between the two approaches is probably the best policy.

COLOR THERAPY	SHIATSU	PHYTOTHERAPY
A discipline that studies and employs the effects of colors on the human psyche. According to practitioners, warm colors like red, yellow, and orange may stimulate growth and healing. Cooler colors like blue and violet are inhibitors, and neutral shades of green have value principally by aiding relaxation.	A form of traditional Japanese massage related to acupuncture in that it is held that the pressure of the practitioner's fingers along certain points of the body's canals of vital energy can help reestablish the correct balance between Yin and Yang and so cure certain organic disfunctions.	A particular form of herbal therapy that depends on treatment with medicinal plants. Special attention is paid to the exact part of the plant used—leaf, root, seed, stem, and so on—with the intent of using these products of nature to reestablish a natural balance within the body.

Aluminum (Aluminium)

In 1884, work on the Washington Monument was finally completed. The needle-shaped structure, rising more than 555 feet (170 m) was built from granite blocks faced with slabs of Maryland marble. As a testament to America's great esteem for its first president, the architects decided to crown the memorial with a pyramid of metal then as costly as silver. That metal was aluminum. The 100-ounce (2,800 g) structure was such a novelty that crowds gathered to admire it when it was displayed in the windows of Tiffany's, in New York City, before its installation.

Two years later, a method was found of extracting aluminum (aluminium in the British commonwealth) from ore that would ultimately make it one of the cheapest and most versatile of metals. Its shining surface coats asbestos firefighting gear and space suits, reflecting light and heat and keeping the wearers cool. Because of its light weight, it is found in the hulls of racing yachts and in the mobiles of sculptor Alexander Calder. In pots and pans, it is an excellent conductor of heat; in wire and cables, it conducts electricity. Because it can be as strong as steel at one-third the weight, it is indispensable in constructing aircraft bodies and skyscrapers like the World Trade Center in New York City. Aluminum is used in foil for its flexibility and in jewelry for its ability to be polished and dyed. Finally, and most important for its future use, it is the most recyclable of all metals.

In the 18th century, chemists began to suspect that clay contained another metal as yet undiscovered. This mysterious metal resisted the efforts of generations of chemists to isolate it. In the early 19th century, the Danish physicist Hans Christian Oersted, a pioneer in electromagnetism, succeeded in producing a few tiny and impure specks. Because Oersted's method involved many steps of mixing and burning an aluminum compound with other chemicals, aluminum could be produced only on a very small scale. Thirty years later Napoleon III, with visions of French armies clad in aluminum armor, financed aluminum research in an attempt to improve refining techniques and reduce the cost. Although production costs dropped from $115 to $17 a pound by 1859, the apparent impossibility of large-scale production kept aluminum from being more than a curiosity.

In 1886, a breakthrough was made with a process called electrolysis, a method of separating chemical elements by passing

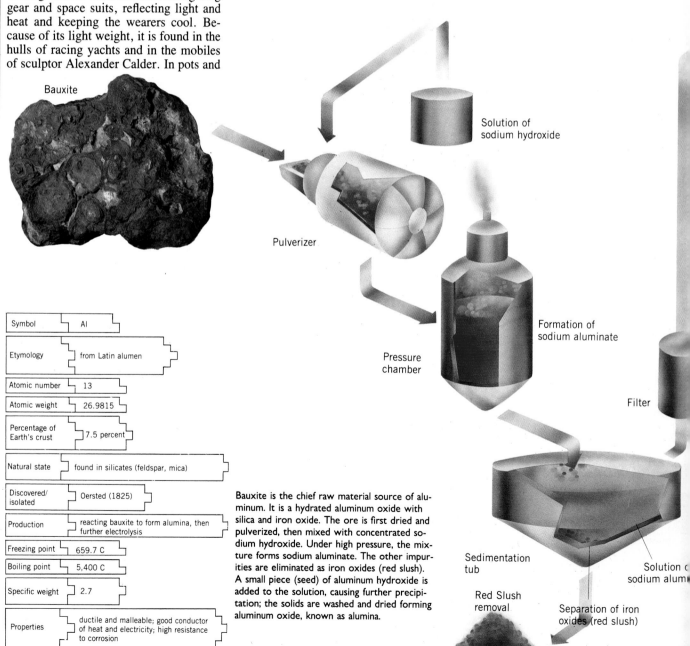

Bauxite

Symbol	Al
Etymology	from Latin alumen
Atomic number	13
Atomic weight	26.9815
Percentage of Earth's crust	7.5 percent
Natural state	found in silicates (feldspar, mica)
Discovered/ isolated	Oersted (1825)
Production	reacting bauxite to form alumina, then further electrolysis
Freezing point	659.7 C
Boiling point	5,400 C
Specific weight	2.7
Properties	ductile and malleable; good conductor of heat and electricity; high resistance to corrosion

Solution of sodium hydroxide

Pulverizer

Formation of sodium aluminate

Pressure chamber

Filter

Sedimentation tub

Red Slush removal

Solution of sodium alumin

Separation of iron oxides (red slush)

Bauxite is the chief raw material source of aluminum. It is a hydrated aluminum oxide with silica and iron oxide. The ore is first dried and pulverized, then mixed with concentrated sodium hydroxide. Under high pressure, the mixture forms sodium aluminate. The other impurities are eliminated as iron oxides (red slush). A small piece (seed) of aluminum hydroxide is added to the solution, causing further precipitation; the solids are washed and dried forming aluminum oxide, known as alumina.

an electric current through a solution. It relies on the fact that certain compounds ionize when dissolved in certain kinds of liquids. An ordinary atom has no charge because the equal amounts of positive and negative charges in it cancel each other out. When a compound dissolves, some of its atoms gain or lose one or more of their orbiting electrons, or negative charges. The balance is thereby disturbed, and each of these atoms or molecules now carries a charge and is called an ion. If electrons are gained, the charged ion is negative; if they are lost, the charged ion is positive.

This condition can occur when a substance is dissolved in a liquid. For instance, aluminum oxide, called alumina, is composed of two atoms of aluminum and three of oxygen, written in chemical notation Al_2O_3. When it is dissolved in a liquid called cryolite, a certain percentage of the Al_2O_3 molecules break apart into atoms of aluminum and atoms of oxygen. The oxygen atoms gain extra electrons, while the aluminum atoms lose some of theirs. The cryolite solution, therefore, contains dissolved within it a large number of Al_2O_3 molecules, a small number of positively charged aluminum atoms, and a small number of negatively charged oxygen atoms.

Electrolysis takes advantage of this situation to separate chemicals. Two sticks of carbon, called electrodes, are put into a conducting solution, and a current is passed between them, so that one electrode has a positive charge and the other a negative charge. The positive aluminum ions move toward the negative pole, and the negative oxygen ions migrate to the positive pole.

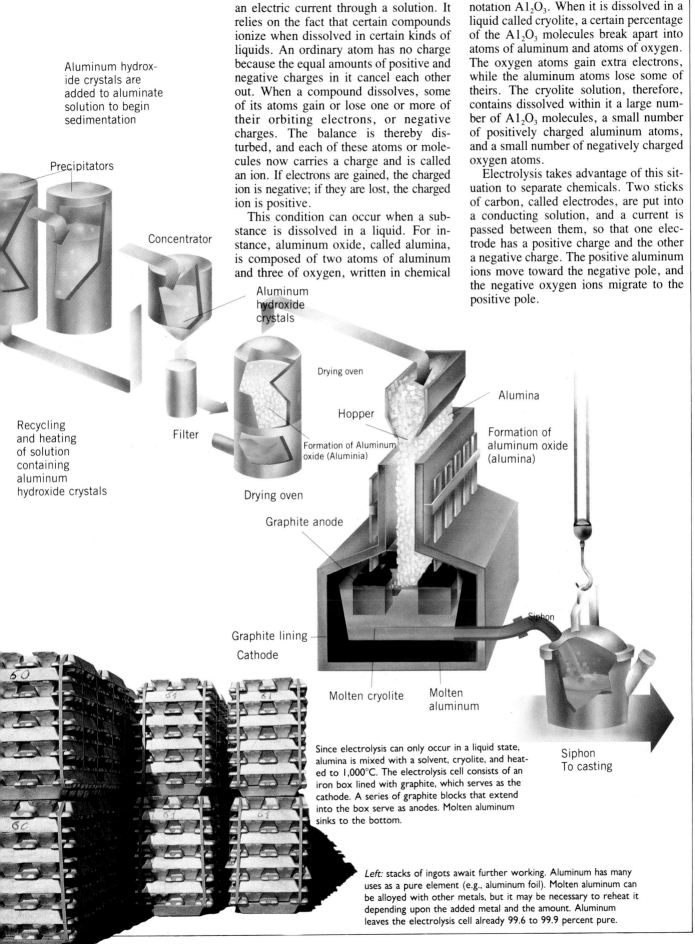

Aluminum hydroxide crystals are added to aluminate solution to begin sedimentation

Precipitators

Concentrator

Aluminum hydroxide crystals

Recycling and heating of solution containing aluminum hydroxide crystals

Filter

Drying oven

Formation of Aluminum oxide (Aluminia)

Drying oven

Hopper

Alumina

Formation of aluminum oxide (alumina)

Graphite anode

Graphite lining
Cathode

Molten cryolite

Molten aluminum

Siphon

Siphon
To casting

Since electrolysis can only occur in a liquid state, alumina is mixed with a solvent, cryolite, and heated to 1,000°C. The electrolysis cell consists of an iron box lined with graphite, which serves as the cathode. A series of graphite blocks that extend into the box serve as anodes. Molten aluminum sinks to the bottom.

Left: stacks of ingots await further working. Aluminum has many uses as a pure element (e.g., aluminum foil). Molten aluminum can be alloyed with other metals, but it may be necessary to reheat it depending upon the added metal and the amount. Aluminum leaves the electrolysis cell already 99.6 to 99.9 percent pure.

Electrolysis was first used to extract aluminum in 1886. The first experimenters to do so dissolved alumina in cryolite, then passed a current through the solution, causing small nuggets of aluminum to form on the positive electrode. At the negative electrode, the oxygen atoms combined with the carbon of the electrode to form bubbles of carbon dioxide gas. Those experimenters used batteries, skillets, and gas stoves. Today, powerful currents from hydroelectric dams, huge steel vats, and giant furnaces are used. Thanks to these more efficient processes, the price per pound dropped to a low of 15 cents in the 1940s.

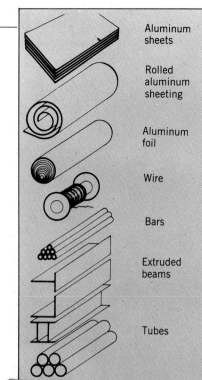

Aluminum sheets

Rolled aluminum sheeting

Aluminum foil

Wire

Bars

Extruded beams

Tubes

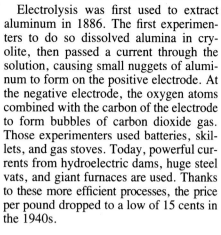

Furnace

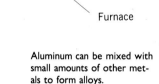

Aluminum can be mixed with small amounts of other metals to form alloys.

The aluminum industry relies on immense quantities of two things—electricity and the mineral source of alumina, an ore called bauxite. Electrical power rapidly is becoming one of the most expensive ingredients in the production of aluminum. The aluminum industry requires more electricity per pound of product than any other. Although small amounts of bauxite are found in North America and in Europe, the main sources are countries near the equator.

Like iron and most other metals, aluminum in its pure form is relatively soft—soft enough to whittle. Also, like iron, it owes its extraordinary versatility to the various properties it acquires when varying amounts of different elements are mixed, or alloyed, with it. Copper makes it stronger. Boron increases its ability to conduct electricity. Magnesium makes it corrosion-resistant, so that it can be used around water, as in boat hulls and kitchen utensils.

One very strong and light alloy of aluminum, duralumin, is made with small portions of copper, magnesium, and manganese. As strong as steel but three times as light, duralumin was invented by the German engineer Alfred Wilm and was used in German Zeppelins during World War I. Since then, even stronger and lighter alloys have been developed, and aluminum alloys are now an indispensable aircraft material. Plans are being made for the first space station to be built of girders made from aluminum ribbon 6 inches (150 mm) wide and 0.03 of an inch (0.76 mm) thick, which will be unwound from spools.

While almost all of the energy involved in aluminum production goes into separating it from the ore, when aluminum is recovered from cans and other scrap, this refining process is no longer necessary. This is quite an advantage; steel, for example, must be put back through the same smelting process by which it was made. For this reason, aluminum is an energy-saver—recycling requires only 5 percent of the energy used to produce the same amount of aluminum from bauxite.

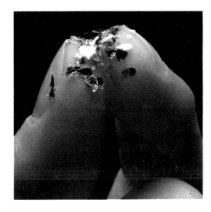

Today, much research is being done in the field of special alloys to find materials that are both light and durable. At right, three-stage Saturn V rocket being launched; missile rockets, satellites, and other space vehicles utilize aluminum alloys. Above, extremely thin pieces of aluminum obtained through a new process of rapid solidification which makes possible the production of a new series of durable, super light alloys.

Ambulance

When the call came through that a man was stuck in a chimney, a New York City ambulance team figured that someone was playing Santa Claus. Instead, the victim was a burglar, and the corpsmen did double duty by extricating him, then calling the police to arrest him. All calls are not of life-and-death urgency, but an ambulance corpsman must always be equipped to save a life, if a life can be saved.

In most places, ambulance vehicles and corpsmen fall into two categories: basic life-support systems manned by emergency medical technicians (EMTs) and advanced life-support systems manned by paramedics. EMTs are trained to treat obstetric, respiratory, and circulatory emergencies as well as burns and trauma, which includes shock, fractures, and some internal injuries. Their work can entail delivering a baby, giving oxygen or clearing an air passage for someone who is suffocating, stopping bleeding, immobilizing a broken bone, or applying cardiopulmonary resuscitation (CPR) to victims whose hearts have stopped beating. Two EMTs administer CPR. One gives mouth-to-

mouth breathing, while the other presses rhythmically and with great force on the victim's chest.

EMT Equipment

Emergency medical technicians could not perform these tasks without the equipment in their vehicles. U.S.-state laws specify some 50 items that every basic life-support system must contain. The most frequently used of these articles are the wheeled cot, on which the patient reclines on the way to the hospital; a folding "stair chair" that enables EMTs to carry the patient up and down stairs and through narrow passageways; and a one-piece canvas stretcher, as well as a "scoop stretcher," which is constructed of two vertical metal panels that fit together. Since EMTs are able to slide the panels under the patient from either side of his body, they do not have to lift him as they do when positioning a patient on a conventional one-piece stretcher. The "scoop" is used when the patient has collapsed in a narrow space or is in such severe pain that sliding a conventional stretcher beneath him would be excruciating. Extrication boards, which look much like large paddles, are used to

remove victims from vehicles that have crashed.

Every ambulance contains permanent oxygen tanks built into the vehicle as well as portable tanks and masks that EMTs can take with them to the scene of an emergency. Devices consisting of suction tips affixed to catheter tubes enable technicians to remove substances—such as food, objects, or vomit—from a suffocating victim's throat. A backboard, to which the patient can be strapped in either a sitting or recumbent position, is used to immobilize the spine; splints are used to hold broken arms and legs. Sandbags are used to immobilize the hip region. Various tapes, bandages, lubricated packs, shears, and gauze pads are used for dressing wounds and burns. Childbirth supplies, including gloves, umbilical clamps, a suction bulb, and sanitary napkins, as well as a stethoscope, blood pressure cuff, bedpans, and linens, are also on board every ambulance.

Emergency medical technicians must complete a state-approved training course, which consists of classroom work and practice, before they may be part of an ambulance corps. They must take re-

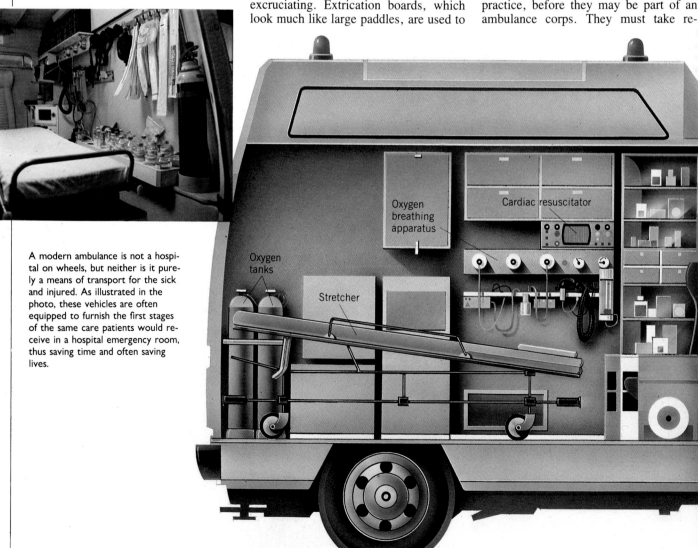

A modern ambulance is not a hospital on wheels, but neither is it purely a means of transport for the sick and injured. As illustrated in the photo, these vehicles are often equipped to furnish the first stages of the same care patients would receive in a hospital emergency room, thus saving time and often saving lives.

Oxygen breathing apparatus

Cardiac resuscitator

Oxygen tanks

Stretcher

fresher courses at appointed intervals and may specialize in areas such as extrication burns, fractures, and so on.

Paramedics

In instances where the treatments permitted to EMTs are inadequate to save a life, paramedics are called to the scene. Unlike EMTs, paramedics may administer intravenous fluids; give drugs; perform intubation, which consists of inserting a tube into a passageway, usually the throat, to permit the flow of air; perform defibrillation, or the electric shock treatments given to victims of cardiac arrest for whom CPR was ineffective; and draw blood samples. Since they may perform these functions only under the supervision of a physician, advanced life-support system personnel must be equipped with direct communication devices—in addition, of course, to containing the items found in a basic ambulance. They must also be supplied with telemetric equipment that automatically transmits an EKG reading taken on the scene of an emergency to a coronary-care unit in a hospital.

In medical emergencies, time is of the essence. Basic and advanced life-support systems are allotted 3 minutes to get underway after a call comes in. Most corpsmen agree, however, that taking much over a minute and a half is unnecessary. Ambulance corpsmen generally spend no more than 10 minutes at the scene of an emergency and 10 minutes at the hospital. Generally, one relative is permitted to ride with the patient to the hospital, and there is always a chair next to the cot for this purpose. A patient may request to be taken to a specific hospital; corpsmen will oblige if they can get there in less than 10 minutes and if the patient's condition does not require a hospital's immediate attention.

Not all the equipment an ambulance carries is for medical treatment. The hacksaw, hatchet, and other tools (right) serve to extract accident victims from wreckage.

When distance is a problem and transport by road would take too much time, helicopters may be used to move accident victims. Helicopters can also carry the emergency room to the patient when large-scale disaster strikes, as with the portable Lifeshelter unit shown at far right.

Below: Cutout illustration of an ambulance equipped with cardiac resuscitation devices to treat victims of heart attack.

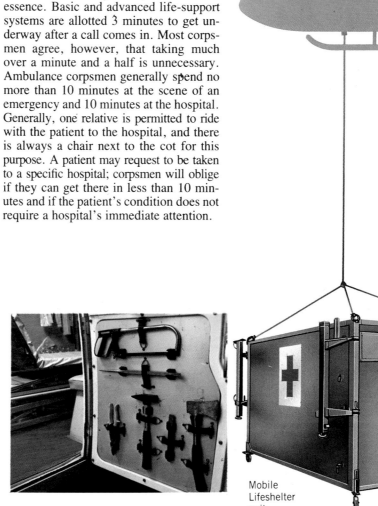

Mobile Lifeshelter unit

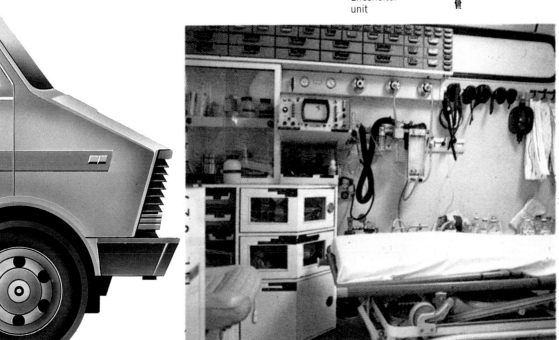

Amines and Amides

Most people know ammonia as an ingredient of household cleaners—the liquid that cleans windows and floors and leaves behind a penetrating odor that makes your eyes water. To organic chemists, however, substances derived from ammonia are among the building blocks of life, the chemical basis for dozens upon dozens of different compounds that are found in all living creatures. Two of the most important amino-acid derivatives are amines and amides; both of them, but particularly the first, play an important part in the building up of proteins, the complicated substances of which cells are made. Amines are also common industrial chemicals. Often-seen examples include aniline, the base for many dyes; a naphthylamine derivative, the principal in-

of the carbon atoms are also bonded to hydrogen atoms. An example is the phenyl group (C_6H_5), where every carbon in the benzene ring but one is bonded to an H atom. (Since both alkyls and aryls contain carbon, they and the amines they form are organic compounds. Most carbon-containing substances are called organic chemicals, because carbon plays such an important role in life.)

Types of Amines

The group of atoms replacing the hydrogen atom is known as a radical, and depending on whether there are one, two, or three radicals, the amine is a primary, secondary, or tertiary amine. An example is aniline, a colorless, oily liquid that is the base for such dyes as aniline black and

medicine used to shrink varicose veins. The second member of the family, diethanolamine, is ($HO-CH_2-CH_2)_2NH$—that is, the same thing as ethanolamine, except that a second hydrogen atom has been replaced by the $HOCH_2CH_2$-chain. Similarly, triethanolamine is ($HO-CH_2-CH_2)_3N$. All three have the same basic Y-shaped structure as ammonia, but the two arms and the upright have been replaced by groups of other molecules. When the alkanoamines are strung together in a different way, the long chains of molecules thus produced are useful as wetting agents for such common chemicals as insecticides, engine coolants, floor waxes, and polishes of various types. In addition, triethanolamine, as stated above, is a common ingredient of antifreeze.

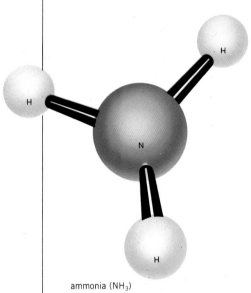

ammonia (NH₃)

gredient in common rat poisons; and triethanolamine, one of the antifreeze constituents that inhibits corrosion of your car's radiator. Two others are cadaverine and putrescine, which, gruesomely enough, are responsible for the odor of rotting bodies.

Ammonia consists of one nitrogen atom and three hydrogen atoms and has the chemical formula NH_3. Ammonia molecules are roughly shaped like a capital Y, with the nitrogen in the middle and the hydrogens at each end. If one or more of the three hydrogens is replaced by a group of atoms called an aryl or an alkyl group, the resulting molecule is an amine.

Alkyls are mixtures of carbon and hydrogen with the general formula C_nH_{2n+1}. When, for example, n is 2, the formula becomes $C_2H_{2(2)+1}$ or C_2H_5—or, as it is commonly called, methyl. Others include neopentyl (C_5H_{11}) and isobutyl (C_4H_9). Aryls, on the other hand, consist of hexagonal rings of six carbon atoms (called benzene rings), in which most but not all

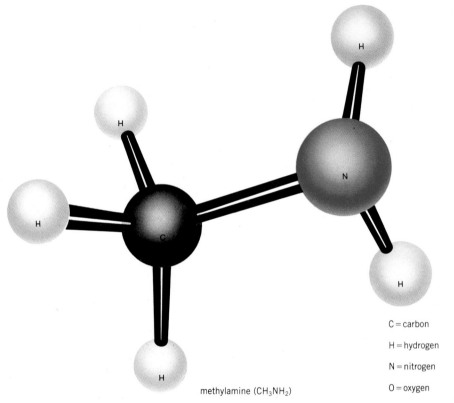

methylamine (CH₃NH₂)

C = carbon

H = hydrogen

N = nitrogen

O = oxygen

aniline red, which are used in the textile and ink industries. It is a primary amine with the formula $C_6H_5NH_2$, which means that one of the three H atoms in NH_3 has been replaced by the aryl radical C_6H_5 (phenyl). If a second radical, the alkyl group C_2H_5 (methyl), takes the place of one of the remaining pair of hydrogen atoms, the resultant secondary amine, $C_6H_5NHC_2H_5$, or ethylaniline, is formed.

Another useful family of chemicals is known as the alkanoamines. The primary alkanoamine, ethanolamine, is made by bonding the chair $HO-CH_2-CH_2$, a type of alkyl group, on NH_3, producing $HO-CH_2-CH_2-NH_2$. Ethanolamine is used to prepare ethanolamine oleate or esclerosina, a

Amides

Amides are built in a similar way, by replacing the hydrogen atoms in ammonia with other atoms. The difference is that amide formulas all have an acyl group, rather than aryl or alkyl. Another way of saying this is that amides all have a carbon-oxygen link in them, instead of being created by links among carbon and hydrogen atoms. Chemically, the acyl radical is written R--C, with the R meaning the rest

$$\parallel$$
$$O$$

of the acyl group. The resulting amides are, like the amines, primary, secondary, and tertiary. Only one of the three compounds replacing the hydrogen atoms, however, has to have the acyl group.

An example is acetamide, CH_3CONH_2, which is made by taking acetic acid (CH_3COOH), the acidic component of vinegar, and replacing the OH by NH_2. Another, more complicated amide is urea, a principal component of human urine. Urea is a *diamide*, that is, an amide with two NH_2 groups in it. Its formula is NH_2COHN_2 (or, as it is often written, H_2NCONH_2).

Both amides and amines have many industrial uses, but their principal importance to man is in their role in the structure of the proteins that are the base of life itself. Amines are also essential to amino acids, the building blocks used by DNA and RNA in the business of reproduction, the most urgent task of any creature.

See also AMINO ACIDS; CARBON; DNA AND RNA.

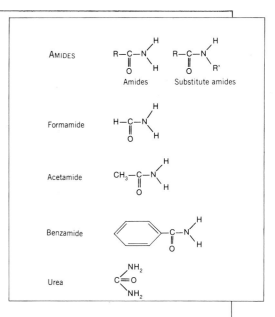

AMINES

Primary   Secondary   Tertiary

Methylamine $CH_3—N$

Dimethylamine CH_3 $N—H$ CH_3

Trimethylamine CH_3 $CH_3—N$ CH_3

Aniline

AMIDES

Amides   Substitute amides

Formamide $H—C—N$

Acetamide $CH_3—C—N$

Benzamide

Urea NH_2 $C=O$ NH_2

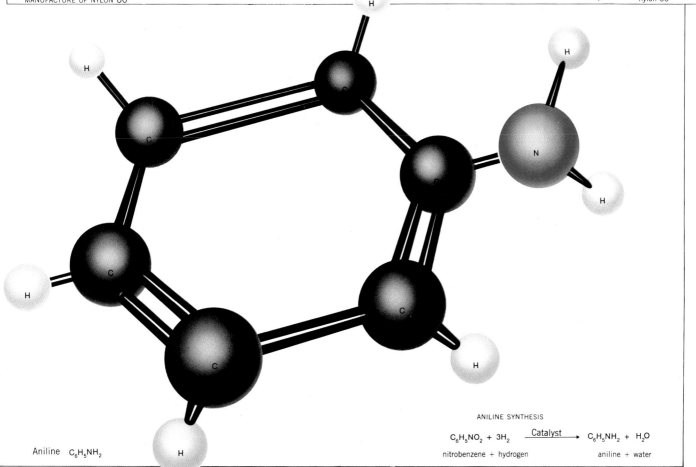

AMIDE SYNTHESIS

$$R—C—OH + NH_3 \xrightarrow{\text{condensation}} R—C—NH_2 + H_2O$$

acid + ammonia   amide + water

$$n\left[HO—C—(CH_2)_4—C—OH\right] + n\left[NH_2—(CH_2)_6—NH_2\right] \xrightarrow{\text{Polycondensation}} —N—C—(CH_2)_4—C—N—(CH_2)_6—N—C—$$

adipic acid + hexamethylenediamine   polyamide (macromolecule containing amides)

nylon thread

MANUFACTURE OF NYLON 66   nylon 66

Aniline $C_6H_5NH_2$

ANILINE SYNTHESIS

$$C_6H_5NO_2 + 3H_2 \xrightarrow{\text{Catalyst}} C_6H_5NH_2 + H_2O$$

nitrobenzene + hydrogen   aniline + water